to Emily and Ella

flora

photographs by nick knight
text by sandra knapp
art direction by peter saville
designed by paul barnes
published by schirmer/mosel

in collaboration with
the natural history museum, london

schirmer/mosel

Preface

All the images of plants in this book are from the herbarium of The Natural History Museum in London. The collection has been made up from many collections, and represents the work of hundreds of botanists.

I was first shown these herbarium specimens in 1992 by Sandy Knapp. I was working on an exhibition at the museum called Plant Power, and we were looking for images for the opening panel of the exhibition. The first one I saw was a plant called *Leucadendron argenteum* – The Silver Tree. This plant looked as if it owed more to science fiction than botany. It was almost two dimensional, shiny as if cast in steel and frozen in white space. I was instantly hooked. I felt as if I had discovered a jewel.

What attracted me the most was the fact that these plants primarily did not look like plants. They made me think of completely different things: some were like feathers, but feathers of neon, laser-drawn, exquisitely refined and breathtakingly delicate. Others were like urban plans, architecturally precise, like cities viewed from the air, infinitely complex. Many were joyful splashes of colour like childrens' paintings, carefree, happy nonsense. I was fascinated. So much of the preconceived imagery I had of plants was reliant on the transient nature of their beauty. Bright colours and wonderful structures which wilt and wrinkle to unrecognisable drably coloured forms.

I was struck by the fact that these plants didn't look dead. Life was very apparent. I could see the movement of the wind blowing through their leaves and petals, sense the water flowing throughout their vessels and their flowers straining to turn and open into the suns' rays. But these plants had one important difference – the fragility, the tragic urgency had gone and they had taken on a new certainty of being; a statement like boldness. They have escaped their fate.

There are few things that make me happier than discovering a new way of seeing the familiar. Seeing in a way I could not have imagined. It is a very liberating feeling and one that makes me very optimistic.

The herbarium at The Natural History Museum contains over six million samples. It has taken over three and a half years to discover the plants for this book. Thousands were taken out for consideration. These were whittled down to hundreds to be photographed. Finally, many extremely difficult and agonising hours were spent selecting the final forty-six. However, I would look forward to each day of searching enorm-ously. It has been a pleasure and a treat to compile this book, and it has been made even more so by the kindness, understanding and encouragement of the botanists at The Natural History Museum, even though I know they realised early on that my criteria for selecting a specimen was wholly unscientific, and that my interest was in looking for the most 'beautiful' examples. I thank them deeply for being so supportive and open to this book.

Nick Knight, London, 1997

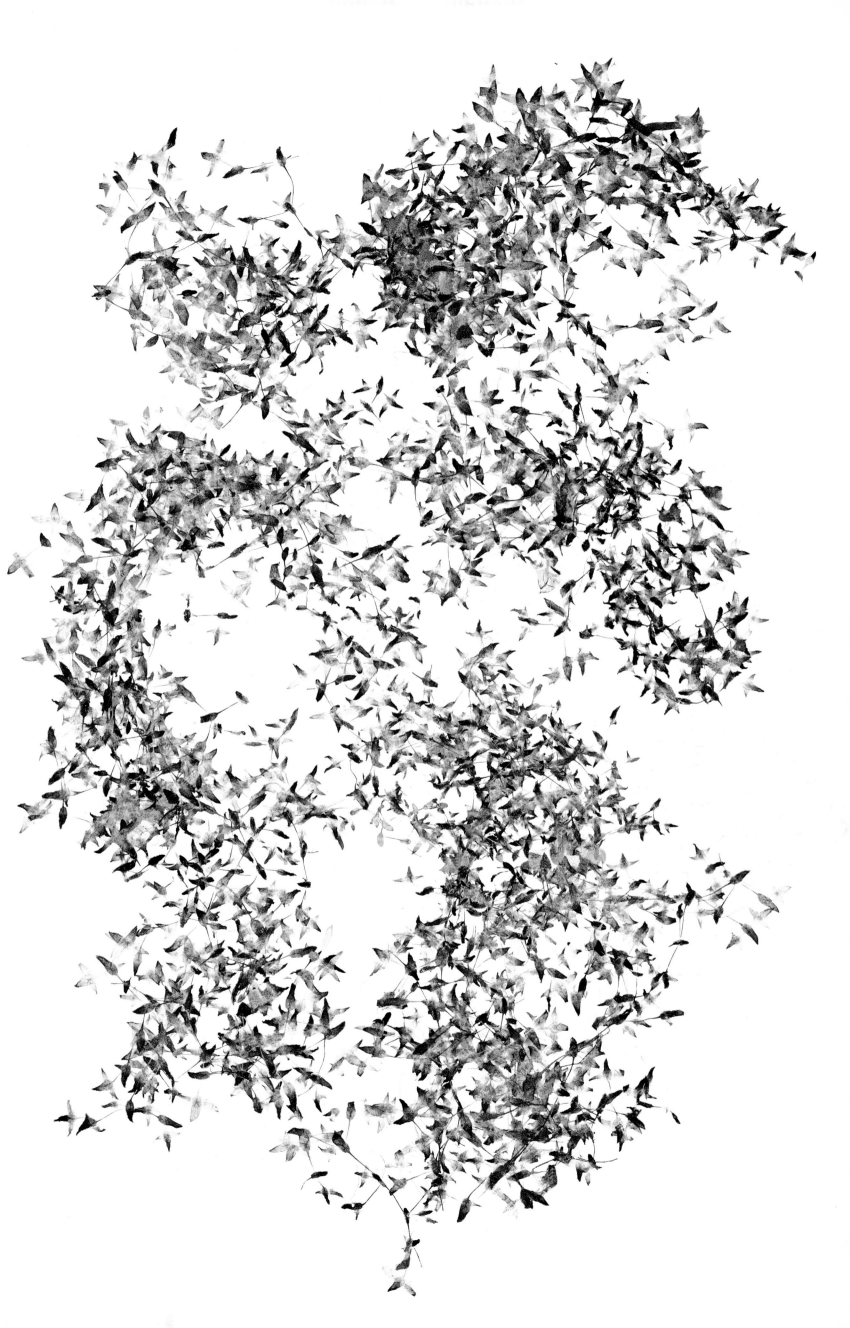

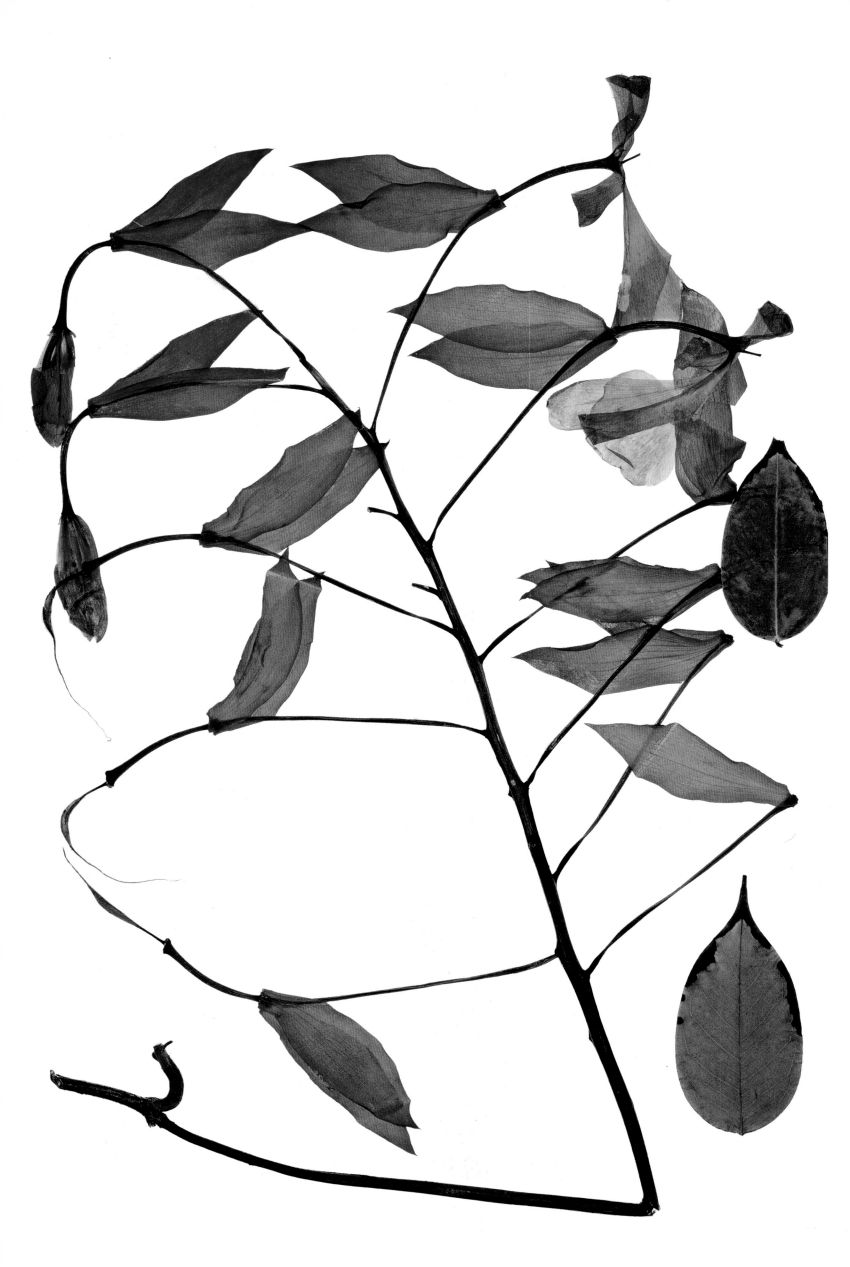

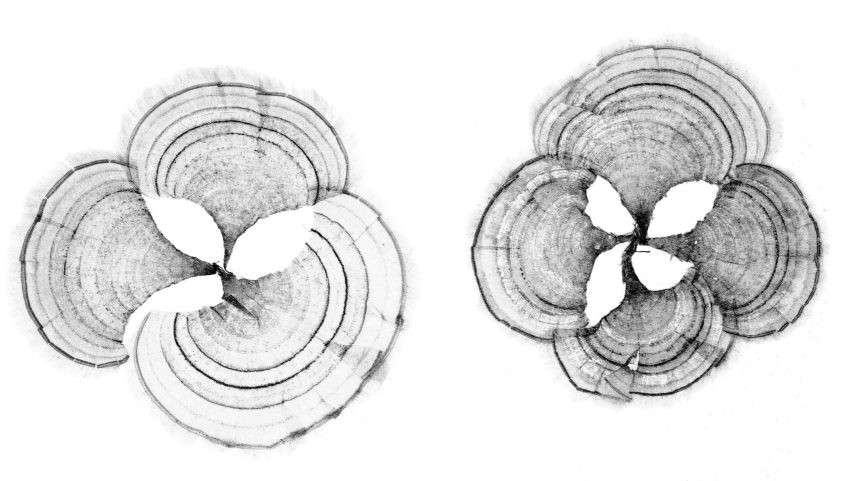
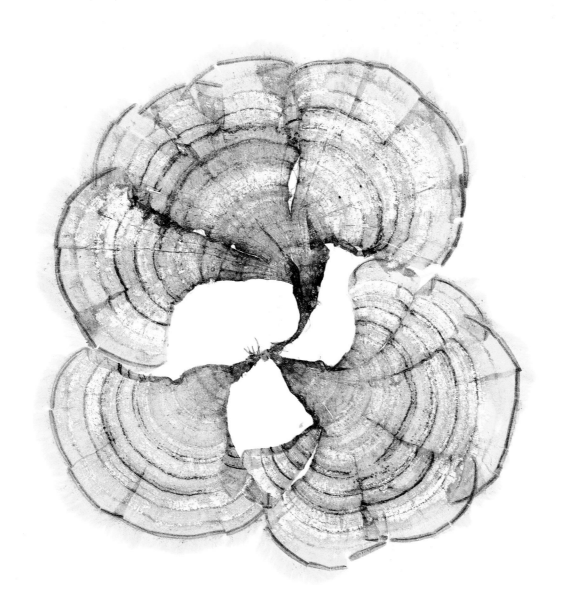

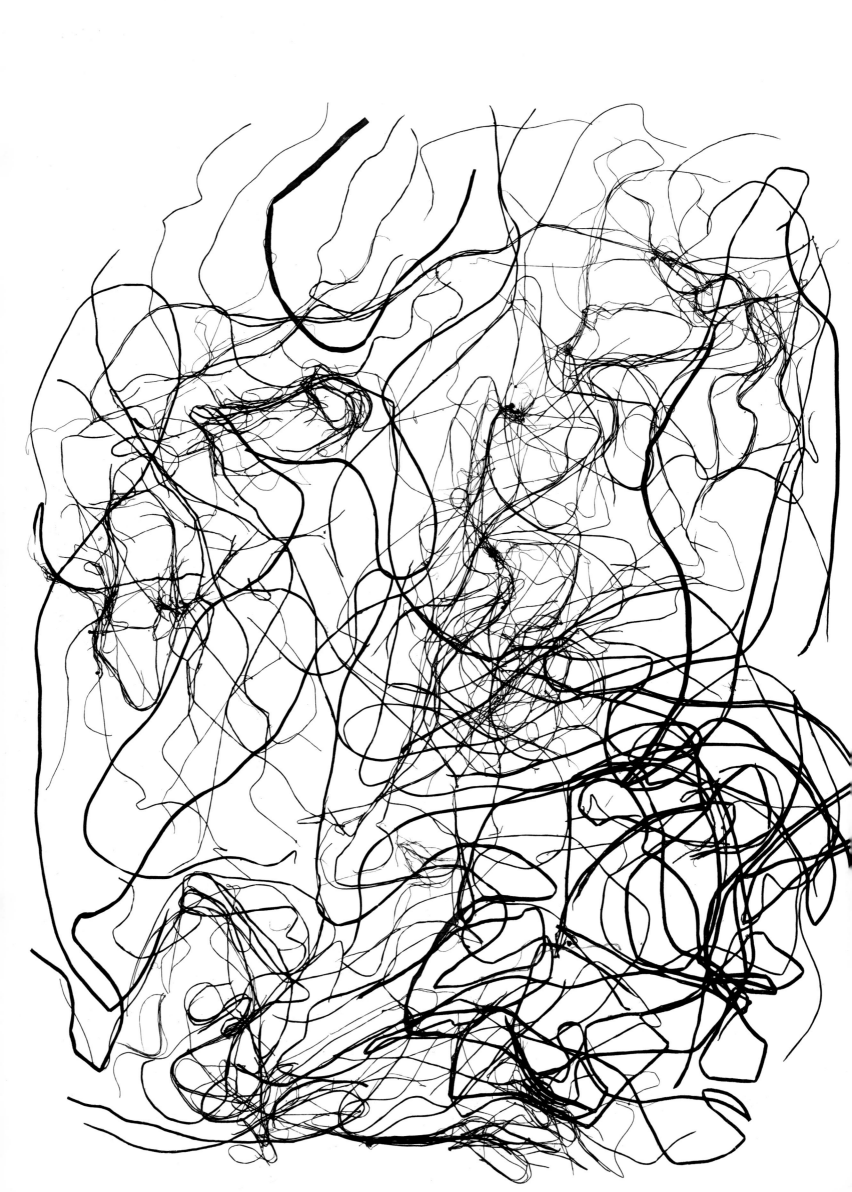

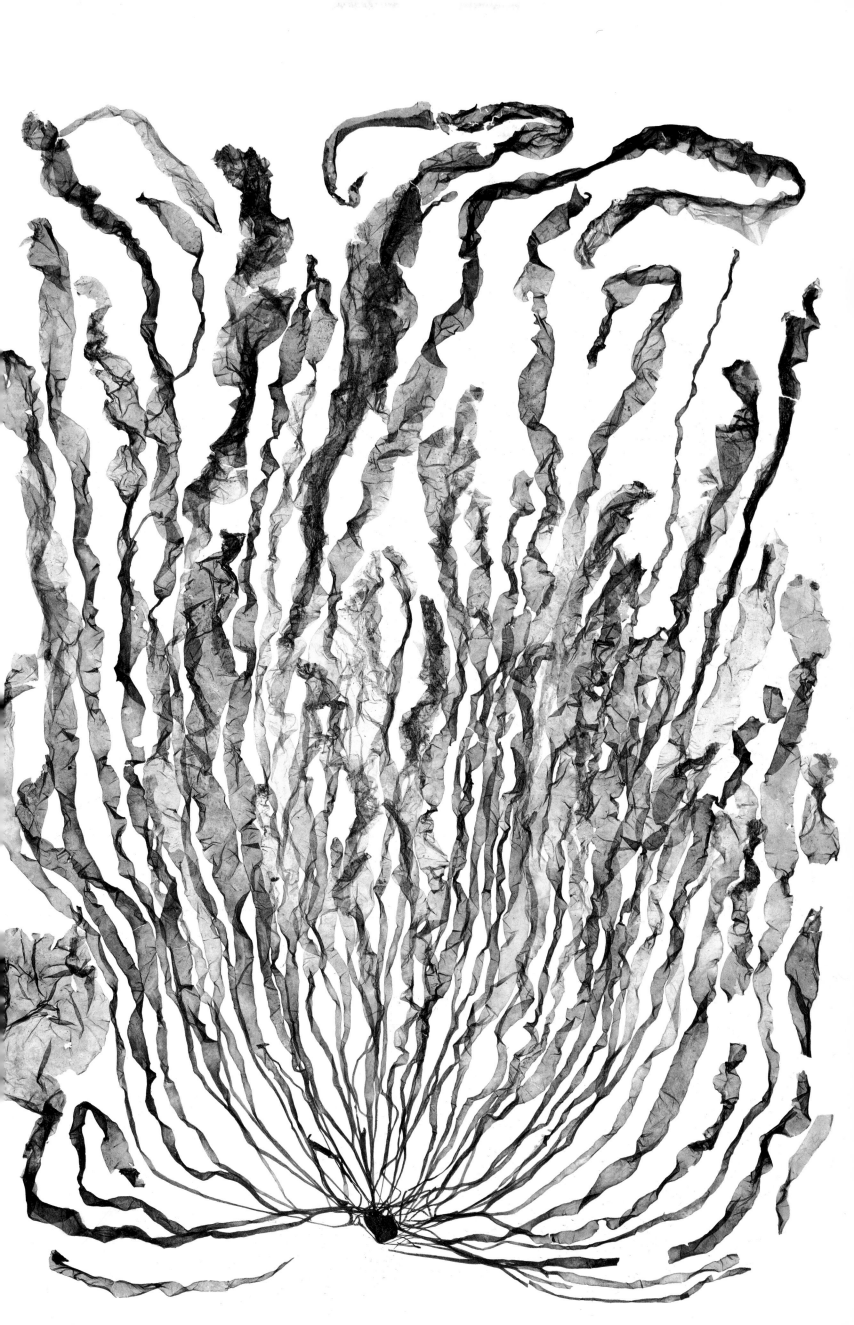

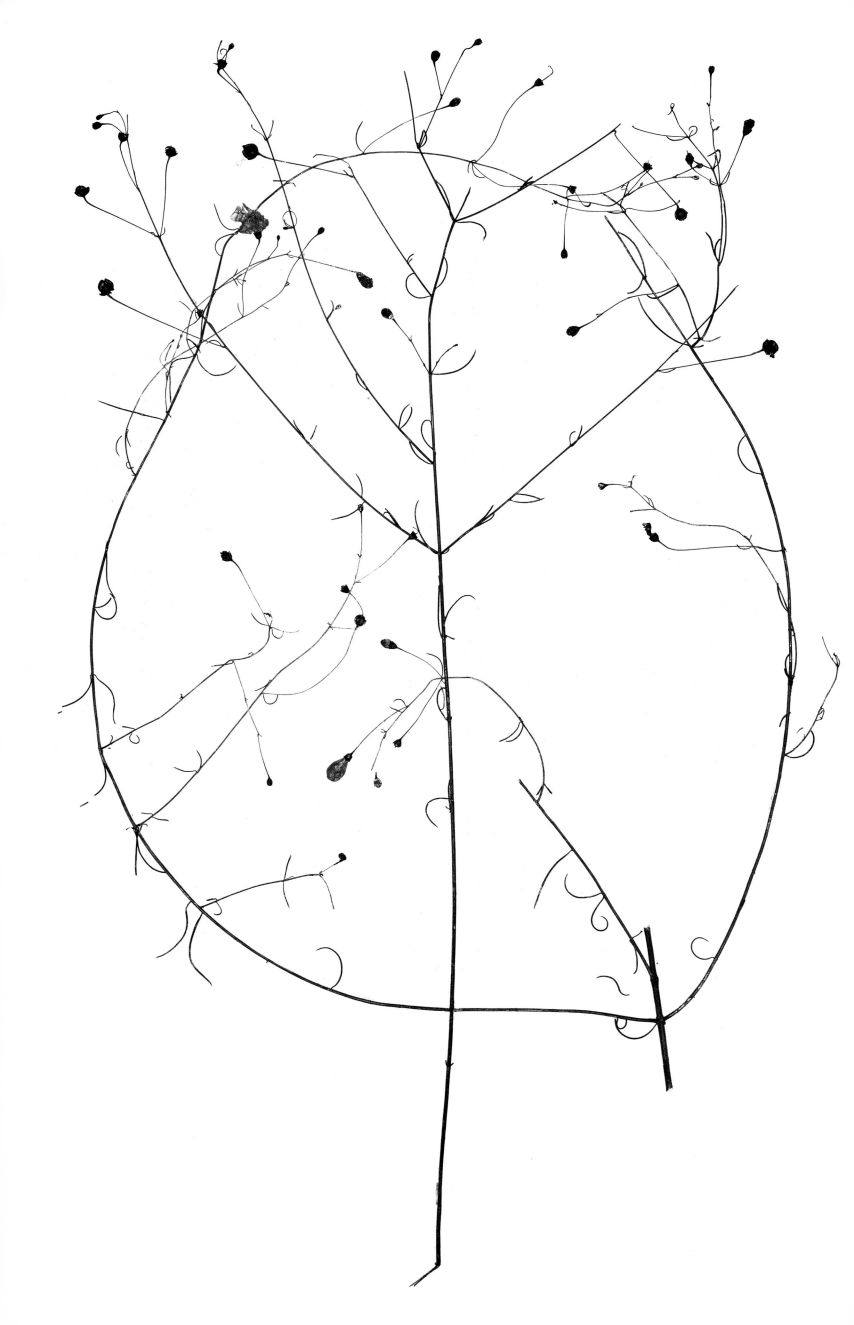

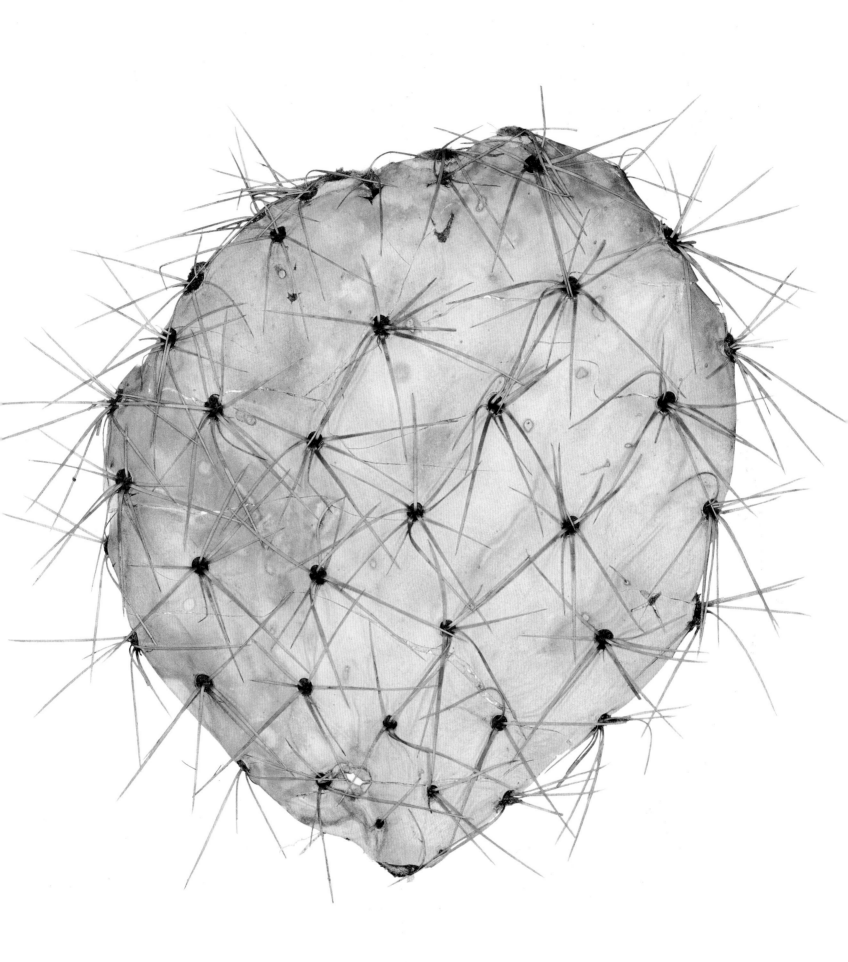

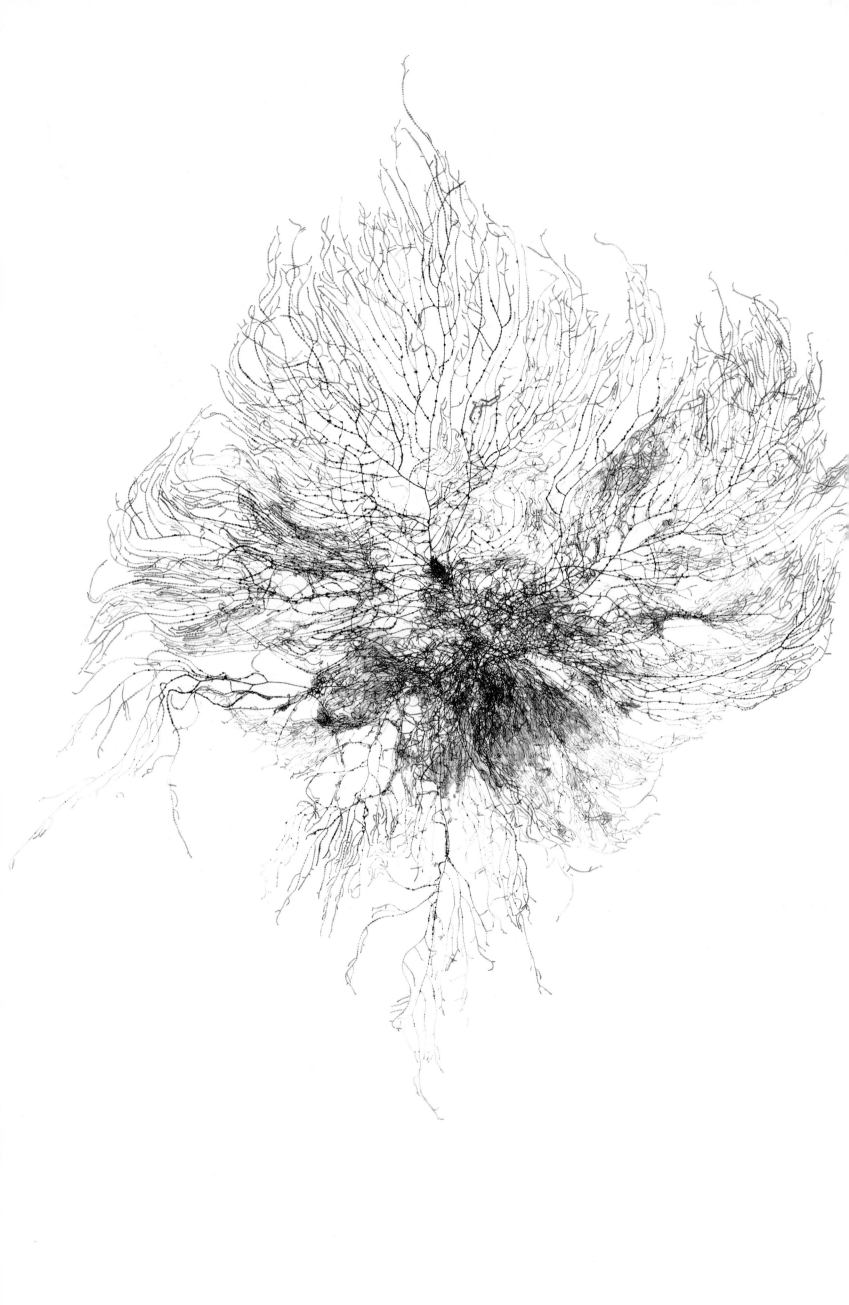

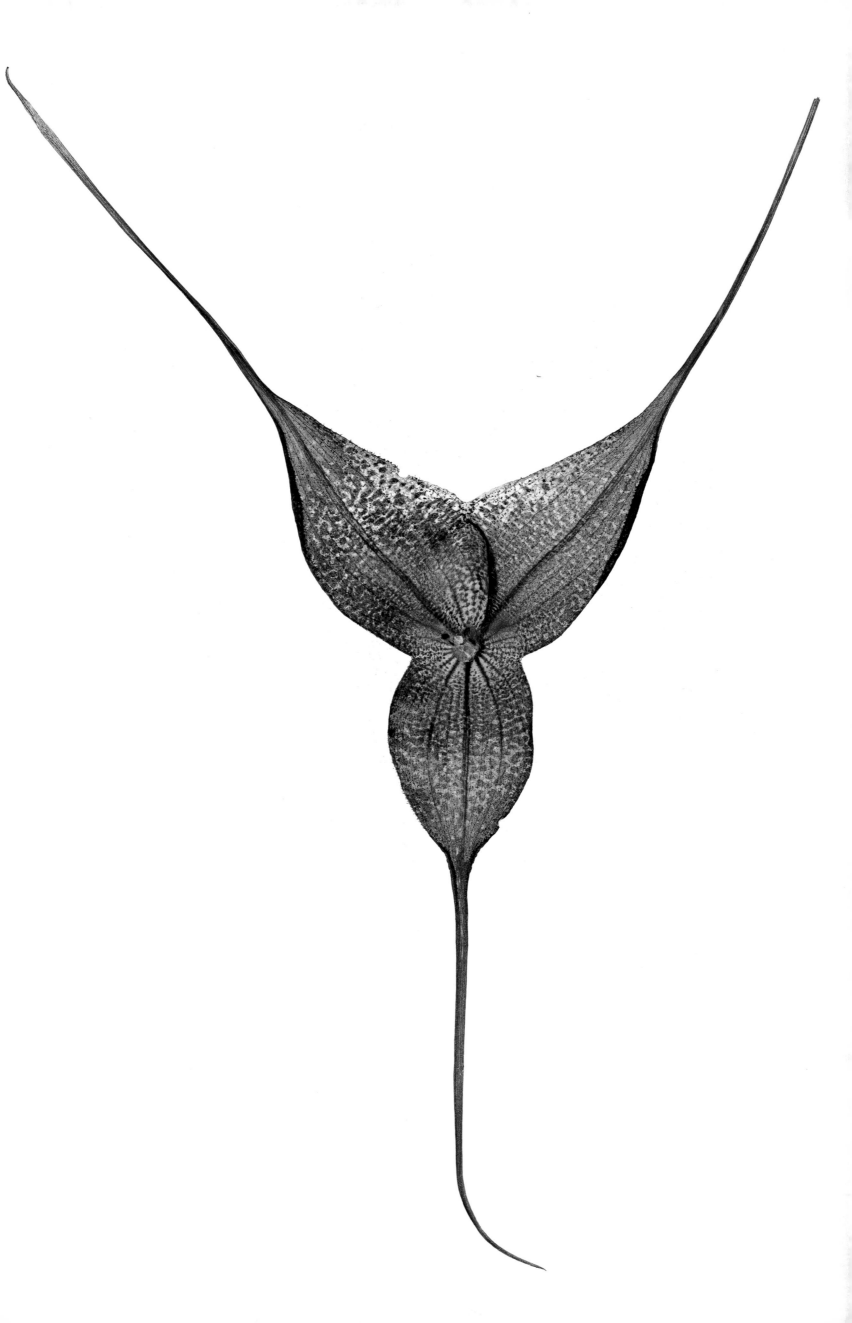

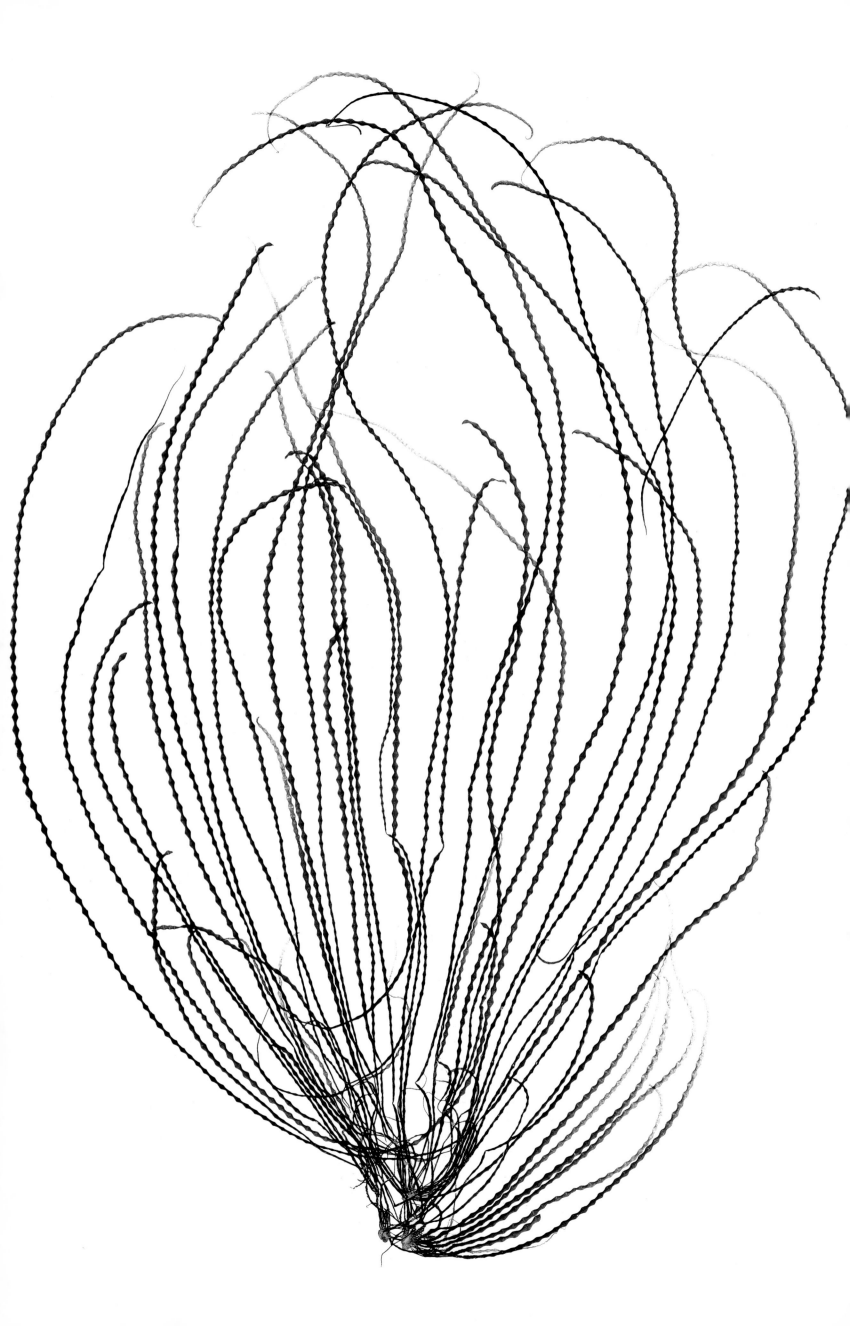

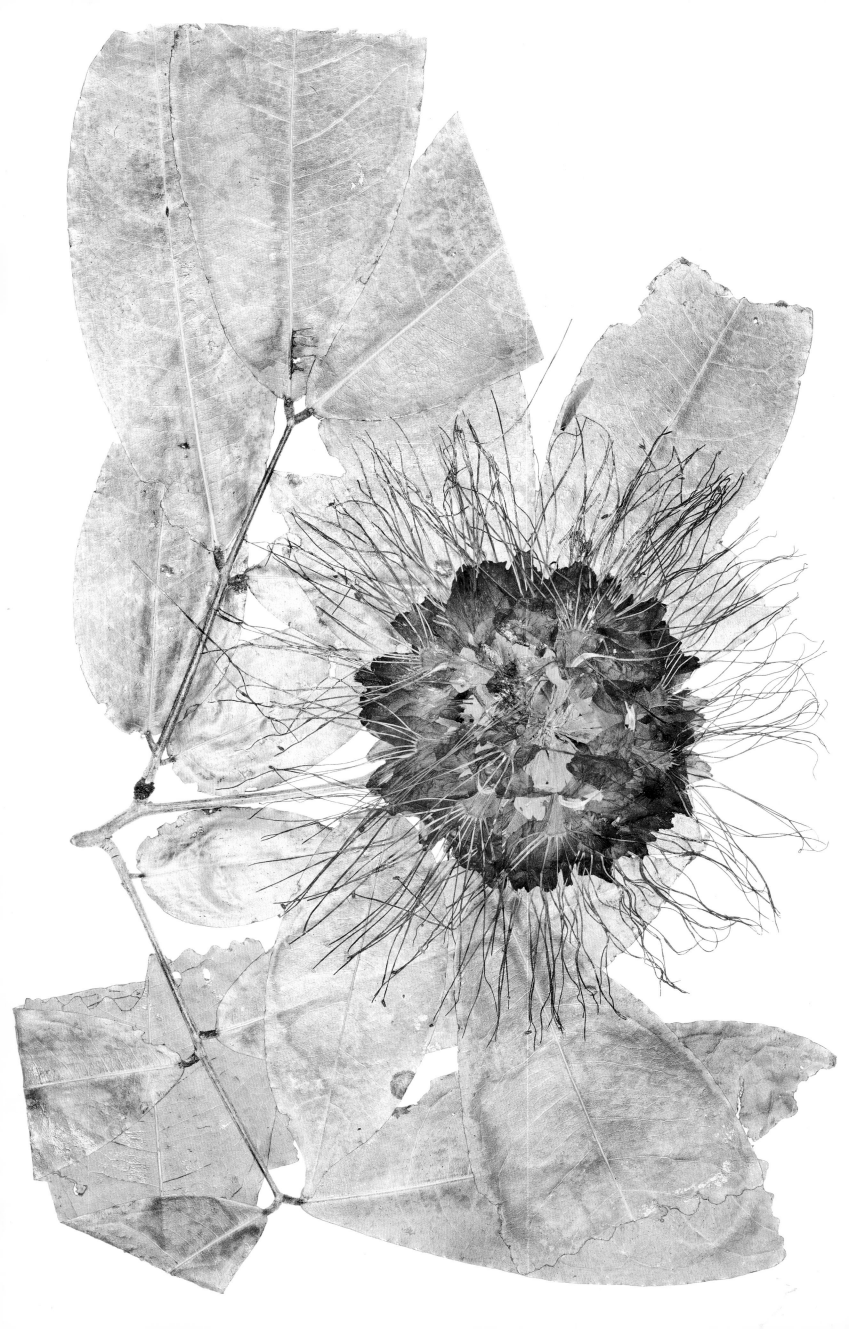

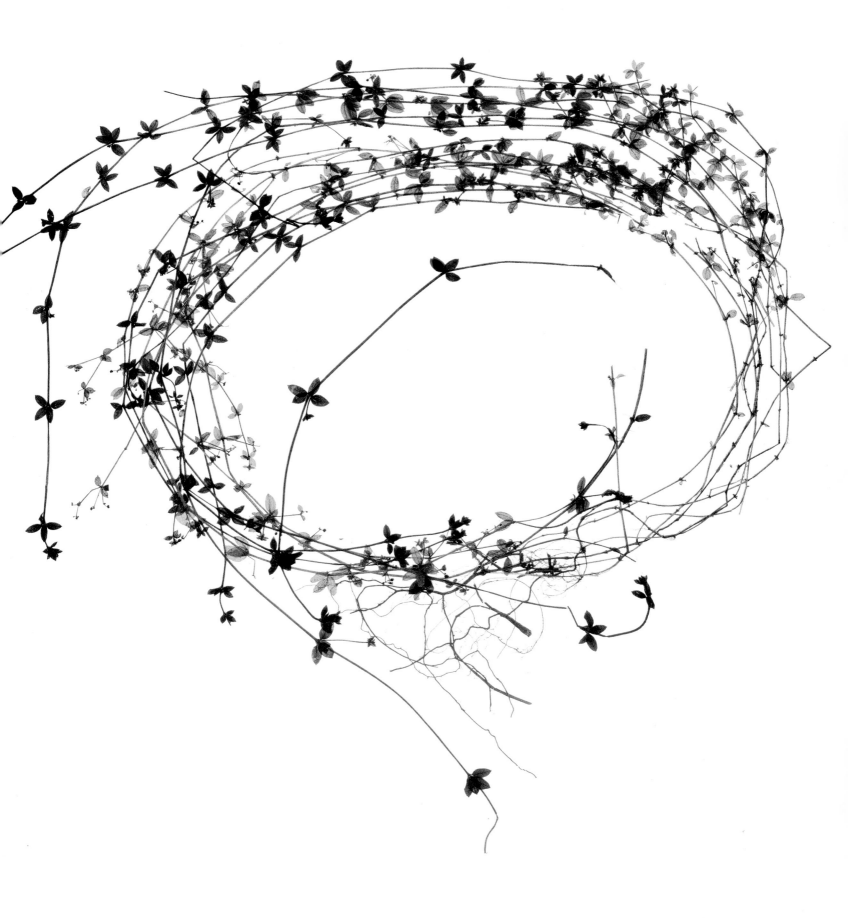

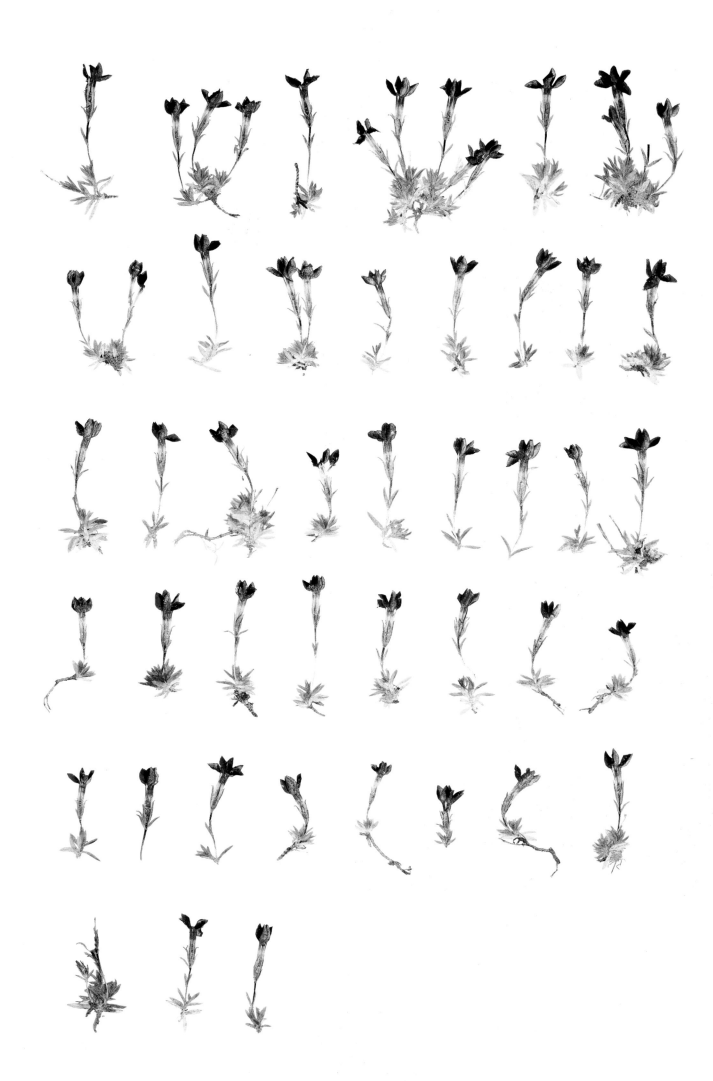

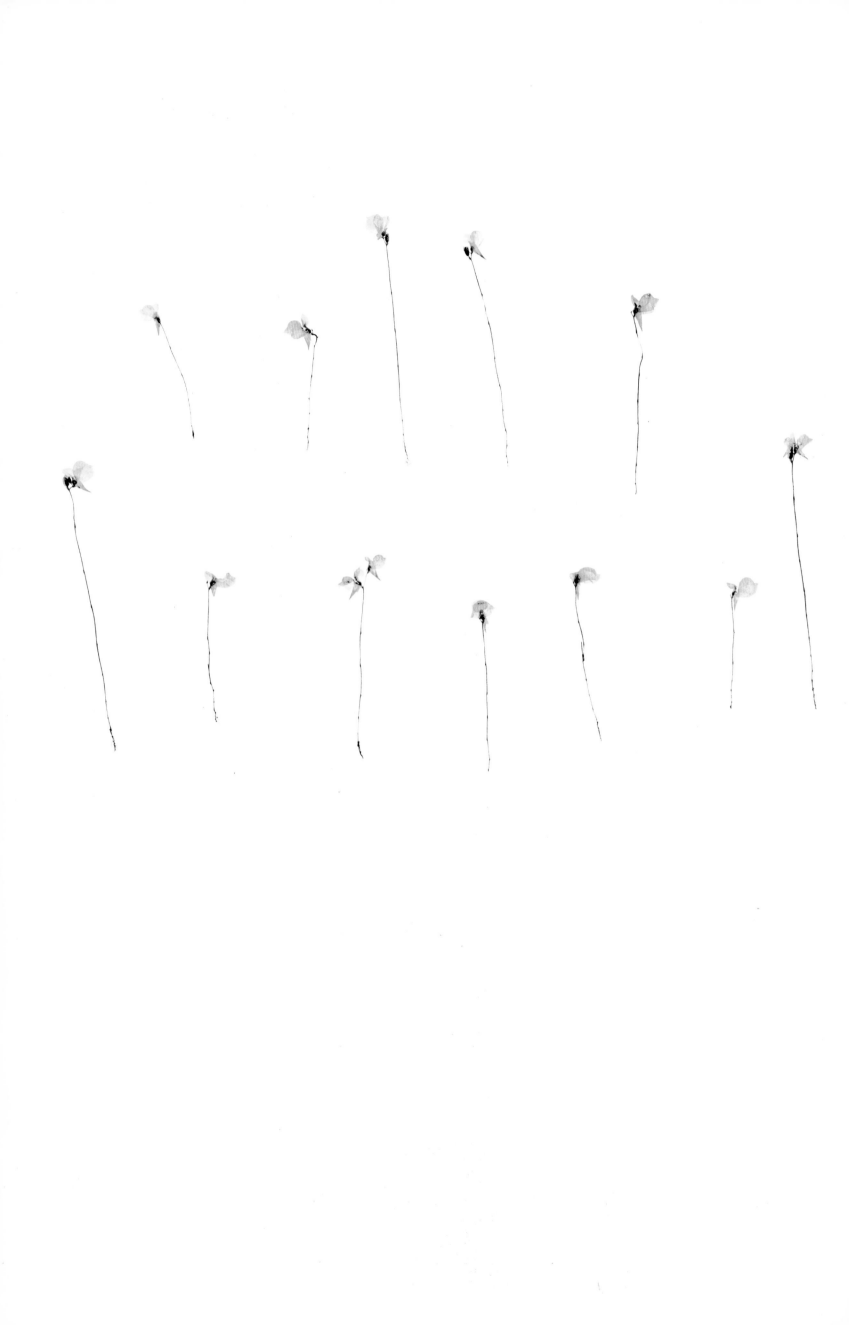

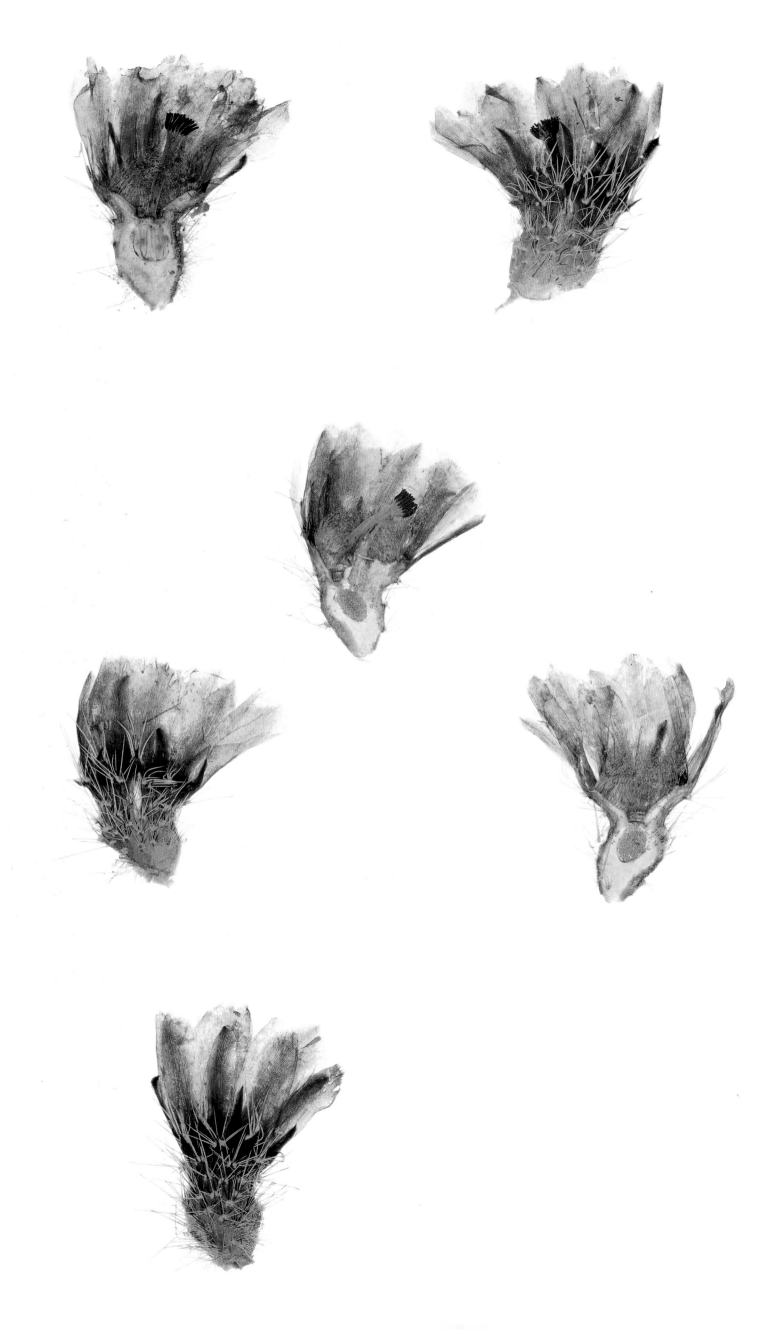

Introduction

Plants have always fascinated people. They feed us, clothe us and are indispensable as drugs and medicines. Botanists are the scientists who study plants, and taxonomists those who name and classify them. To name and classify the diversity of plants that exist in the habitats of earth, taxonomists observe live plants, but just as, perhaps even more, important is the observation of specimens in the herbarium. But what is a herbarium? Herbaria have been likened to 'mortuaries for dead plants' but a much more appropriate analogy is to a library of pressed flowers. A herbarium is a reference collection of the diversity of plants through time, and in space. What is held in the herbarium, instead of books, are specimens. Each specimen is a sample of plant material, pressed flat and dried, to which a label detailing what it is and where it was collected is attached. These specimens are invaluable to the taxonomist – they are the concrete evidence of the occurrence of a plant in a particular place at a particular time. But beyond their utility as scientific tools, herbarium specimens have a peculiar and often breath-taking aesthetic quality – they can be beautiful objects in their own right. It is this beauty we have tried to capture in this book.

The journey from live plant in the forest to dried specimen in the herbarium is long and varied, and has occasionally been filled with drama and adventure. Early plant collectors braved incredible hardship to obtain their specimens – some, such as George Forrest in Tibet, even died in the attempt. Even recently, students on a collecting expedition to Irian Jaya were kidnapped and held hostage for some months before being released unharmed. Botanists accompanied all the major exploration missions to the New World, and the specimens sent back to Europe by the first botanists to visit the Americas astounded the untravelled society at home. But how is a specimen procured and prepared? First, find your plant. If it is a tree, it needs to be scaled, but a herb can be collected in its entirety. A portion is then pressed between papers and dried, either in the open air under weight as was done by early collectors, or over heat, the common modern method. The amount of care taken in the arrangement of the plant as it dries plays a large part in its ultimate utility to the taxonomist, as well as to its eventual appeal as a beautiful object. Each collection, which may consist of several to many duplicate specimens, is given a number, which when combined with the collector's name, makes a unique identifier for that gathering. Notes as to features likely to disappear with pressing and drying – such as plant height and flower colour – are carefully recorded. When all the plants are dry, they are shipped back to the herbarium. Early collectors lost whole plant collections representing months and months of work in shipwrecks, to bandits or to fire. To these collectors, this was a severe loss indeed, as many of them collected for a living, and were paid by the specimen which eventually reached its destination. Even today specimens can get lost in the post, impounded by customs or go up in smoke in an automobile accident. Barring disaster the specimen eventually reaches the herbarium, but without any information attached it is scientifically useless. Once at the ultimate destination the label containing all the information so carefully recorded in the field is prepared and matched, using the unique combination of collector and number, to the plant in question.

The final step in the process of transformation from live plant to herbarium specimen involves some unsung heroes – or more usually heroines. Everyone admires and knows about the collector – they do the adventurous part, going to dangerous and out of the way places, climbing up trees, falling off cliffs, being involved in shipwrecks or attacks by bandits. But back home in the herbarium, it is the plant mounters who take the dried plants, still loose in their papers, and prepare the final specimen that the taxonomist uses and that can be an object of such beauty. The dried plant is arranged on a sheet of high quality paper, then glued down. The label is glued to usually the lower right hand corner, and any loose fragments are put into a tiny packet which is also attached to the sheet. The end result is a herbarium specimen – a permanent record of a plant, where it grew, what it looked like alive, and who collected it when.

The specimens photographed for this book all come from the herbarium of The Natural History Museum in London. The Natural History Museum is justly famous for its collections of animals, both those living today and those that are now extinct, such as dinosaurs. But, unbeknownst to many, the Museum also has a large botanical department. The Museum's herbarium is one of the larger herbaria in the world, and with some six million specimens, is an incredibly valuable resource to not only the taxonomists who work in it, but to scientists world-wide. Two major collections form the historic basis of the herbarium –

that of Sir Hans Sloane and that of Sir
Joseph Banks. Sloane was a physician and
a president of the Royal Society and the
British Museum was founded to house his
amazing and enormous collections of
plants, animals and objects of historical
interest. Sir Joseph Banks was also a president of the Royal Society and a physician,
and travelled widely collecting both animals
and plants. The greatest adventure of his
life however, was his voyage as the ship's
naturalist aboard the *Endeavour* with Cap-
tain Cook. His collections were incredibly
rich and valuable, and he bequeathed them
to Robert Brown, who was to give them
eventually to the British Museum (the
natural history collections of which were to
become The Natural History Museum).
Brown gave the collections to the Museum
during his lifetime, and became the first
Keeper, or head, of the Botanical Department. The tradition of field exploration and
addition to the collections persists to this
day, with the herbarium being enriched
by the efforts of many botanists through
the years.

The specimens we have chosen to
reproduce here have been chosen not for
their scientific value, but for their beauty
and aesthetic appeal. They represent only a
fraction of what lies behind the doors of The
Natural History Museum's herbarium and
even a smaller fraction of the specimens in
the herbaria of the world. Each specimen
has a story – in reality many stories. The
lives and adventures of those involved with
the collection and preparation of each of
those reproduced here would fill many
volumes – but we have tried to lead the
reader down one of the many avenues that
emanate from a simple pressed flower.

For Alfred, Isabel & Victor
Sandra Knapp, London, 1997

1 Leucadendron argenteum   2 Nymphaea norchali

PROTEACEAE:
Leucadendron argenteum (Linnaeus)
R. Brown, South Africa, collected by J. Bowie, 1817-1822, (male plant)

Leucadendron argenteum, the silver tree, is one of the beautiful species that inhabit the South African fynbos – the most species diverse habitat on earth. The term fynbos is derived, perhaps, from early settlers' perception of it as worthless and full of timber too slender for harvesting – 'fijnbosch'. Fynbos is a vegetation type – a collection of plants – dominated by evergreen shrubs and characteristic of South Africa's south-western and southern Cape region. The hot dry summers and cool rainy winters create a mediterranean climate and the poor soils and adverse conditions have influenced the development of a unique and beautiful flora. Early plant explorers in South Africa were fascinated by the strange and unusual plants there and sent many back to botanical gardens and museums in Europe. The first European illustration of a fynbos plant, a member of the Proteaceae – the family to which the silver tree belongs, was published in 1605! Fynbos is also rich in geophytes, or bulbous plants. Our garden gladiolus originates from a fynbos species as do many other astonishingly beautiful bulbs. Geophytes are able to withstand the periodic fires that sweep the fynbos, while many of the proteas only release their large seeds from closed woody cones when stimulated by fire. This allows the seedlings to establish in a nutrient rich, competition free environment. Fire is now used deliberately in the management of fynbos, as some rare species were declining towards extinction in its absence. Without fire, there would be no fynbos. The extraordinary diversity and beauty of this unique vegetation is still as fascinating to botanists today as it was to the first European botanists to set foot on the shores of the Cape.

Death by waterlily – it sounds like the title of a melodramatic opera – but it is a fact of life for the insects that pollinate these most spectacular of flowers. The flowers' size, colour and scent make them attractive to humans and insects alike, and they are masters at handsome advertising. Insect visitors come for the copious pollen offered by the waterlily flowers in the male stage of their development. The stamens are crowded in the centre of the brightly coloured flower and shed pollen for three or four days running. Each night, as the temperature drops, the flower closes, then reopens the next morning with a new load of abundant sticky pollen. The waterlily appears to be a reliable and abundant source of nutritious food – pollen is high in nitrogen and is eaten by flies, bees and beetles, all of whom visit the flowers and carry pollen on their bodies from flower to flower. But the happy scene of satisfied pollinators and pollinated flowers is only part of the picture. On the first day of its life the waterlily flower is in the female phase of its development and the stamens shed no pollen. Instead they form an erect ring around a circular pool of liquid in the centre of the flower. The inner ones are coloured yellow, the colour of shed pollen, but it is fakery. At the bottom of the pool is the stigma into which pollen grains must grow to fertilise the flower. Insects visiting the flower seem oblivious to the subtle difference in shape on this first day and clamber about looking for pollen. But teetering on the edge of the yellow centre, they find, not the masses of sticky pollen they seek, but a slippery, waxy surface devoid of any grip and leading straight into the fluid filled depths. If an insect ventures too far, in it goes! The fluid contains a wetting agent and since the waxy surface of the ring of closed stamens offers no grip to aid the trapped creature to climb out, even the smallest insect soon sinks and drowns. Any pollen sticking to its body from a previous visit to a male stage waterlily flower is washed off, sinks to the bottom of the pool to the stigma and fertilises the flower. The waterlily flower then closes for the night, and when it opens the next morning the stamens have closed over the pool and begun to shed their pollen. The waterlily now wears its more benign and kinder face, more in keeping with our sense of its beauty.

NYMPHEACEAE:
Nymphaea norchali Burmann f. var. *caerulea* (Savigny) Verdcourt, African lakes, collected by W. A. Cunnington 52, 20 April 1905

PASSIFLORACEAE:
*Passiflora
alato-caerulea* Lindley,
cultivated in New York,
collected by
L. J. Magrum 101,
14 September 1972

The 'flos passionis' or Passion flower has long been a symbol of Christian faith and belief. In 1610 Jacomo Bosio, a monastic scholar in Rome writing a treatise on the Cross of Calvary, was shown drawings of a wonderful flower by an Augustinian friar of Mexican origin. At first he did not believe the flower was real, as its form was so fantastic that he felt it must be exaggerated. In the end the evidence was overwhelming, and he felt it his duty to present the miraculous story of the Passion flower to the world. He saw the flower as representing not only the Cross of Calvary, but also the past mysteries of the Passion. The form of the flower was laced with meaning: the central column represented the Cross itself, the corona filaments were the plaited and twisted crown of thorns (in his original drawing the filaments were 72 in number, as were the thorns in the crown), the three stigmas represented the three nails driven into Christ's body, the five blotches at the base of the column were the stains of the blood from the five wounds Christ received. In Bosio's original description the leaves were described as lance-shaped and marked with dots representing the thirty pieces of silver paid to Judas Iscariot. The Passion flower was seen as a sign of the 'Croce triofante', the assurance of the ultimate triumph of Christianity. People of the time were deeply versed in the doctrine of signatures, where every plant had a special purpose and this purpose was revealed in its shape or form. Thus the Passion flower's use as proof of the revealed truth of the wonderful and mysterious workings of God would have been implicitly believed by most people. Later authors had to change the story to fit the species of *Passiflora* they had at hand, but the essentials remained the same. In later versions, the ten petals and sepals were said to represent the ten apostles present at the Crucifixion, and the three large floral bracts of *P. caerulea* were representative of the Trinity. The potent symbolism of this most peculiar of flowers remains to this day, with *Passiflora* in today's language of the flowers symbolising Christian faith and, more ironically, credulity.

Duckweeds, the round green blobs floating on pond surfaces all over the world, are in fact among the tiniest of flowering plants. The entire duckweed plant is composed of more or less plate-like bodies, called fronds. The fronds often reproduce vegetatively by budding and are usually found clustered together in floating mats. The plants sometimes bear tiny roots – but the tiniest duckweed, *Wolffia*, the plants of which are less than 1.5 mm long, doesn't even have those. In the frond is a small pouch where the flowers are borne. Incredibly, the duckweeds have flowers grouped into inflorescences, sometimes two or three flowers per pouch! A male flower consists of a single stamen, and a female of a single naked ovary with one ovule. When the plants bear fruit, each one has a single seed. Not obvious flowers, but definitely there! The relationships of the duckweeds are difficult to determine since the plants themselves are stripped to the bare essentials. Botanists think they are related to the philodendron or arum family, the Araceae, based mainly on evidence from seed and pollen development and structure. Their very peculiar and distinct appearance however sets them apart form all other flowering plants – it is amazing to think that even such a tiny flower as this still performs all the same functions for the plant as does a rose or a lotus. Efficiency and results are the important factors in reproduction, not size.

LEMNACEAE:
Lemna trisulca
Linnaeus, British Isles,
collected by
J. E. Dandy 815,
23 May 1943

5   Amherstia nobilis

6   Eryngium foetidum

LEGUMINOSAE:
Amherstia nobilis
Wallich, cultivated in
Dominica, collected by
C. Whitefoord 6124,
15 April 1988

Botanists name plants after people for many different reasons – to curry favour, to honour patrons, to commemorate the collector, or sometimes just to express admiration or show solidarity. The noble Amherstia, *Amherstia nobilis*, was named by Nathaniel Wallich, the curator of the Calcutta Botanical Garden from 1815 to 1827, after the Right Honourable Countess Amherst and her daughter Lady Sarah Amherst 'the zealous friends and constant promoters of all the branches of Natural History, especially Botany...'. The elder Lady Sarah Amherst, later the Countess Amherst, was the wife of the Governor-General of India under George IV. She and her daughter botanized extensively in the Himalayas and were responsible for the introduction of several widely cultivated plants, among them *Clematis montana*. They shared their enthusiasm for botany with Nathaniel Wallich, and brought him many plants for the Calcutta Botanical Garden. Wallich had heard of a splendid tree growing in Burma from one of his friends, a Mr. Crawfurd, who brought him a few dried flowers, a leaf and an intriguing description of a tree growing in a monastery garden, covered with pendulous geranium-coloured blossoms, which were scattered at the feet of the images of Buddha by the monks as daily offerings – 'too beautiful an object to be passed unobserved even by the uninitiated in botany.' Wallich tried in vain to obtain more material or information from other travellers, and finally, in 1826 to 1827 on his last botanical journey in India, he travelled as a part of the mission of the Supreme Government of British India to the Court of Ava in Burma. In March of 1827 he visited the same monastery as had Crawfurd, and to his delight, found the tree, in full vermilion bloom. Wallich described it in the most glowing terms, calling the tree 'unequalled in the Flora of the East Indies and I presume, not surpassed in magnificence and elegance in any part of the world' and 'the most strikingly superb object which can possibly be imagined.' It is a sign of the great esteem in which he held the Countess Amherst and her daughter that he named such a spectacular plant after them. Wallich obtained some branches of the tree and established it in the Gardens in Calcutta, from whence it has been spread in cultivation all over the tropics. *Amherstia nobilis* is propagated primarily by layering, thus a tree now in cultivation may in fact be the very plant that so dumbfounded Wallich with its magnificence and beauty.

The buggy taste and odour of cilantro, otherwise known as coriander or Chinese parsley, is delicious to some and anathema to others. It is definitely an acquired taste and both the seeds and the leaves have long been important both as a spice and as a medicine. A native of south-eastern Europe, coriander's name comes from *koris*, or bedbug, a reference to the distinctive buggy smell of the crushed plant. Coriander seeds were used in love potions in the Middle Ages and were recorded as a potent aphrodisiac in the Thousand and One Nights. Gripe water, the mother's friend, has coriander seeds as one of the active ingredients and the seeds were often used in potions against flatulence and other stomach problems. Since its introduction from the Old World, coriander has become an important component of Mexican and Peruvian cooking, but before its arrival a plant with a similar buggy odour and taste was already widely in use as both a spice and medicine. *Eryngium foetidum*, or culantro as it is known throughout Latin America, with its large simple leaves at the base of the plant and spiky groups of flowers, looks very different from coriander with its finely divided leaves and delicate inflorescences. But its uses, both as a seasoning and as a medicine are strikingly similar. Cilantro leaves are used to flavour foods and are also, like coriander, widely used as a cure for stomach problems such as flatulence, gas and diarrhoea. But culantro has wider uses too, it has been shown to be effective as an anti-malarial and is used as a cure for obesity in some parts of Central America. The convergence in use is surely due to the similar, if not identical, chemical constituents of the plants themselves as evidenced by their similar buggy smells. The finely divided, tender and easily chopped leaves of coriander have largely replaced the tougher, somewhat spiky leaves of culantro in cooking, but culantro remains an important dooryard medicinal in most of Latin America.

APIACEAE: *Eryngium
foetidum* Linnaeus,
Mexico, collected by
C. L. Smith 1067,
April 1895

7 Pulmonaria longifolia   ## 8 Padina pavonica

BORAGINACEAE:
Pulmonaria longifolia
(Baster) Boreau,
cultivated in England,
collected by
C. C. Lacaita,
15 November 1919

Science and superstition have always co-existed uneasily. Galileo's forced recanting of the sun-centred universe to the Inquisition was triumph of superstition over science, but recent advances in the identification of the genes causing disease are triumphs of science over superstition. Pseudo-science comes under the heading of superstition – and was as prevalent in the past, perhaps even more so, as it is now. Medicine is rich ground for pseudo-science to flourish, as it often proceeds by trial and error. For example, much of the time the effects of drugs or treatments are observed, but mechanisms are not clearly understood. In the sixteenth and seventeenth centuries some commercial herbalists (effectively the pharmacists of today) popularised the ancient belief in the Doctrine of Signatures. The Doctrine of Signatures held that plants must have been placed on Earth for use by man, thus cures for diseases prevalent in certain areas would be found in those areas. Signs and symbols present on a plant would indicate the disease for which the plant was the cure – 'by the outward shapes and qualities of things we may know their inward Vertues, which God hath put in them for the good of man.' The doctrine, although not formally conceptualised until the Renaissance, was possibly used by the Chinese, the ancient Hebrews and Hippocrates and the ancient Greeks. Renaissance practitioners of the doctrine of signatures believed for example that walnuts, which looked like a brain, were useful in treating brain disease; henbane, whose fruits looked like a row of teeth, was useful in treating toothache; and heart's-ease, shaped like a valentine heart, was useful to stimulate the heart. Lungwort has somewhat elongate leaves, thought to resemble a section through a lung. Since the leaf itself is spotted, this, using the doctrine of signatures, indicated that it ought to be used for the treatment of tuberculosis – which caused a spotting of the lung tissue. Unfortunately, the vast majority of plants described as having particular signs under the doctrine of signatures do not have the purported medicinal value. Lungwort is one of those that at least partly works. Silica in the leaves helps to restore the elasticity of the lung tissue and reduces bronchial mucus. Unfortunately its use as a cure for tuberculosis was merely wishful thinking – in the pre-antibiotic age, death from consumption was only a matter of time.

Controversy and inconsistency were hallmarks of Col. Richard Meinertzhagen's complex life. The second son of an eminent banking family, he was forbidden to pursue his chosen career as a zoologist and became, in the words of David Lloyd George, 'One of the ablest and most successful brains I have met in the Army.' Throughout his career in the Army he continued to follow his life-long passion – natural history. He served in East Africa during the first years of World War I, there acquiring a reputation for innovative daring and exceptional blood-lust. Despite being intimately involved in the brutal put-down of a tribal rebellion against British rule, he admired the East African tribespeople greatly for their courage and natural intelligence. He disapproved of the large scale take-over of African land by white, mainly British, settlers, predicting trouble in the future. He spent much of his later army career in the Middle East – where again he showed the enigmatic and seemingly contradictory nature of his character. He was keen on Arab autonomy in the Holy Land, but despised Arab 'laziness, deceit, greed, dishonesty and treachery'. But he also closely identified with the lifestyle and love of freedom of Arab desert nomads. Even more enigmatic was his strong stand on Zionism, views which eventually alienated him from many of his army colleagues. While staunchly supporting the Jewish Zionist cause – he professed an admiration for Adolf Hitler! After retiring from government service Meinertzhagen devoted himself to natural history – particularly ornithology. His beautifully prepared plant collection was one of his cherished possessions, and in 1954 he somewhat reluctantly donated it to The Natural History Museum. He also donated the bird collection amassed over many years – but with many strings attached. Although a magnificent collection, doubt exists as to the authenticity of some specimens and often as to the veracity of his observations and labels. This seaweed specimen is surely correctly labelled however – and connects to a most enigmatic incident in Meinertzhagen's career. He was implicated in the botched massacre of a group of Bolshevik spies in Ronda, Spain, in February 1930. Later that year, while on holiday in Jersey, perhaps even while he pressed and arranged this sheet, he received a threatening letter referring to the Ronda incident. Some have suggested he wrote it himself – but the Ronda episode is probably the most mysterious of his complex career. Contradictory and mysterious, Meinertzhagen's life cannot fail to grip the imagination. The sheer beauty of and the care with which he prepared and arranged his plant specimens however are beacons of consistency in an otherwise turbulent life.

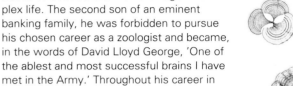

PHAEOPHYTA: *Padina pavonica* (Linneaus) Lamouroux, Jersey, collected by R. Meinertzhagen, May 1930

PHAEOPHYTA:
*Scytosiphon
lomentaria* (Lyngbye)
Link, China, collected
by Rev. Boyden,
anno 1913.

The benefits of seaweeds are manifold and seemingly unending. You can use them as face masks, shampoo your hair with them, use them as body-building supplements, fertilise your garden with them, use them as medicines, and above all, eat them. Seaweeds are technically macro-algae and are common on coasts all over the world. The weight of the mass of vegetation, macro- and micro-algae, filling the world's shallow seas greatly exceeds that of all plants on land. Seaweeds have often been cited as the worlds' great unexploited bounty, but many cultures have used seaweed as food for a very long time indeed. Early Chinese records from 3000 BC indicate that the Emperor Shen-nung used seaweeds as both medicine and food. An encyclopaedia from 300 BC, again from China, mentions twelve species useful as foodstuffs. The Korean court regularly traded kelp, agar and nori to the Chinese Imperial court. The Japanese have a well-deserved reputation as seaweed lovers, they use many species and all the main species cultivated in Japan today were listed in the annual tribute to the Imperial Court in the eighth century. The Romans found the Britons using laver (the same thing as the Japanese nori), dulse and carragheen, and stalks of sugar wrack were on sale in Edinburgh markets as late as 1800. Today, seaweeds are making a comeback as health foods. We also eat and often drink them every day without knowing. Alginates and agars, both extracted from seaweeds, are widely used as thickening agents, they stabilise ice-cream and preserve the head on our pint of beer. Sugara, or beanweed (*Scytosiphon lomentarius*), is a tubular brownish green alga distributed widely in the Northern Hemisphere. It has high iron content and when dried has a pleasant bean-like taste, hence its English common name. In Japan it is an important soup ingredient. One can even use the leftover soaking water as a refreshing face wash. Seaweeds may look a bit peculiar and unappetising at first, but they have a long history of culinary use throughout the world.

The graceful floating forms of many types of seaweeds are both mesmerising and attractive. But once out of the water, their supportive medium, they tend to collapse into a gooey, gelatinous mass. How then to preserve both the botanically interesting structures and the lovely form of seaweeds? To make a dry specimen of a marine or freshwater alga requires a bit more patience and cunning than to make one of a 'real' plant. You begin by taking a shallow dish or tray, strong paper, wire mesh, forceps and a soft paint brush, and nylon tights into the field. Then you catch your seaweed, which is sometimes difficult, as they tend to be very firmly attached to rocks. With the tray full of water, you place the paper on top of the wire mesh and immerse it. Then you float the seaweed in the water and tease it with the forceps and paintbrush into the shape you want – hopefully nearly that which it took when alive in the water. Carefully lifting the edge of the wire mesh, the water is drained off, leaving the specimen stuck to the wet paper. At this point minor adjustments are made, then you place the paper onto an absorbent blotter. Most algae are sticky and mucilaginous and so will glue themselves onto the paper – and this is where the nylon tights come in handy! By spreading them on top of the specimen as it dries, you prevent your seaweed from sticking to the underside of the next piece of blotting paper. Once dry, the specimen – if you have been skilled and careful enough – is a true object of beauty. Preparing a specimen of a seaweed is often as much art as science.

CHLOROPHYTA:
*Enteromorpha
intestinalis* (Linneaus)
Link, Isle of Man,
collected by
E. George,
21 August 1895

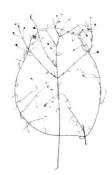

SCROPHULARIACEAE:
Agalinis laxa Pennell,
Florida, collected by
A. H. Curtiss 1910,
in the month of
October between
1884 and 1899

Parasitism is a peculiar way of life. A parasite is wholly or partly dependent upon another organism for its nutrients – in the case of plants, minerals and water from the tissues of the host and energy in the form of sugars from the photosynthetic processes of the host plant. Parasitism is a word with negative connotations – parasites are blood-sucking, destroy their hosts and are generally to be discouraged. But the parasitic way of life is incredibly specialised and terribly efficient, if not the epitome of fair play between organisms. Parasitic plants span a huge range of forms and degrees of dependence – from plants without chlorophyll that are utterly dependent upon their hosts to green plants that look perfectly capable of carrying on the process of photosynthesis for themselves, but yet do not. Most complete, or holoparasites, are brown or yellowish in colour since they lack chlorophyll. They also tend to lack leaves, and some have become so reduced and specialised that the parasite itself consists only of a few flowers that grow out of the stem of the host plant – using precious energy only for the necessities of reproduction! Parasites that contain chlorophyll have been called hemiparasites, half-parasites, but the term is misleading as they draw appreciable amounts of photosynthetic products from the host to supplement their own meagre supply. These plants are hard to spot – they masquerade as a normal everyday green plant going about its business, but can cause untold damage to other plants. Witchweed, *Striga*, is a parasite of maize, sorghum and other commercially important grasses and can cause massive damage to crops. Many members of the snapdragon family are parasitic – Indian paintbrushes (*Castilleja*), rattles (*Rhinanthus*) and the false foxgloves (*Aureolaria* and *Agalinis*) are all hemiparasites, and some botanists even put the obligately parasitic broom-rapes (*Orobanche*) in the family as well. All of these plants are root parasites, and under the soil even those that appear to be living on their own will be attached to a host plant's root system, drawing up nutrients and sugars. The effect of a parasite on its host is to rob it of nutrients, thereby retarding its growth and ultimately destroying it. Perennial parasites 'ration' their hosts, keeping them alive until the parasite itself has completed its life cycle. The host is never destroyed until the parasite has taken all it needs – in a parasitic relationship it is the parasite that is the stronger and more aggressive partner, flourishing at the expense of its host. On the surface, plants all seem very much the same, but the complexity and variety of their lifestyles is truly astounding.

In the early days of specimen collection, plants were pressed flat in blotting papers and then laid out in the sun to dry. The papers had to be changed often, and botanists would spend days tending to their drying plants. The problem of how to press and dry a cactus has vexed many a botany student as well as many botanists unaccustomed to collecting these plants. Since the cactus stem is designed for the storage of water, it is in direct conflict with being pressed and dried. It is quite straightforward today, with forced air heat and rapid drying of plant specimens to dry a cactus or other succulent specimen, but imagine how difficult it must have been for the early collectors. Even now, to properly collect a cactus the botanist must cut the stem in half and scoop out the sticky wet interior. In the early days of plant collecting, salt was often sprinkled on the wet surface to encourage the water out of the tissues. The blotting papers used to press the specimen had to be changed hourly rather than daily, the more usual method, altogether a very time-consuming and laborious process. It is no surprise that few professional botanists specialised in cacti. The spines get in the way as well – and many a botanist has 'prepared' a cactus specimen by crushing the plant under the LandRover toolbox.

CACTACEAE: *Opuntia robusta* Wendland,
Mexico, collected
by F. G. Meyer & D. J.
Rogers 3086,
24 August 1948

HYDRANGEACEAE:
Hydrangea macrophylla
(Thunberg) Seringe
cultivar 'Gentian-Dome',
cultivated at the Hillier
Arboretum, England,
collected by the staff
of the British Museum
(Natural History) 1053,
20 August 1974

Why are some people's hydrangeas blue and others pink? Is it just due to the cultivar, or type, the neighbours have, or should you have planted it next to a buried aluminium teakettle, as the old wives' tale goes? Well, the truth involves a little of both, as truth often does. The mophead, or hortensia, hydrangeas have large, often flat-topped inflorescences of what look like brightly coloured pink or blue flowers. But these florets are sterile – the showy petal-like coloured parts are in fact the calyx (usually green and inconspicuous) and there are no reproductive parts – stamens or ovaries. Occasionally a few small, rather dull, fertile flowers are produced in the centre of the mop, but these do not contribute to the overall colour display or impression of the inflorescence. Some varieties, or cultivars, are bluer or pinker than others but the intensity of blue finally achieved depends upon the availability of aluminium in the soil. The aluminium content of soil, in its turn, largely depends upon soil pH – or acidity. In acid soils (with low pH), aluminium is more available to be taken up by the plant. An aluminium teakettle buried in an acidic soil will lead to the desired blue flowers on a hydrangea growing there. As with so many old wives' tales, there is more than a grain of truth to the story.

Specimens in any given herbarium are all mounted on pieces of paper of a standard size. In Europe, where herbaria have a long and somewhat idiosyncratic history, each herbarium has its own size of paper – at The Natural History Museum in London it is one size, at the Royal Botanic Gardens Kew a little smaller, in Vienna quite a bit larger and so on. In the United States, however, all herbaria use the same size paper – which is of course a different size to any used in Europe! This rather sensible standardisation in the United States is due to the influence of Asa Gray, a Harvard botanist who did much to encourage and open up the study of botany in the United States. But paper size apart, how does a field botanist translate the three-dimensional form of a live plant into the restricted two dimensions of a herbarium sheet? Future users of the specimen need to see both sides of the leaf, preferably several flowers and perhaps a fruit. Sometimes it is easy – for a plant with small leaves some can be turned one way up and others the reverse, so that once the dry plant is stuck down onto the paper both sides of the leaf can be seen. But what about large leaves – ones that are larger than the dimensions of the paper itself? The answer lies in the art of the fold – a little like origami, the ancient Japanese art of paper folding. Extremely large leaves can be cut to fit, but often information about shape is lost in the cutting down to size. Better than cutting is to fold the leaf so that its general shape can still be seen – with a little bit of imagination – and so that both sides can be examined without breaking anything once the plant is glued onto the paper. The end result is a two-dimensional shape that can be translated by the botanist's mind to its original three-dimensional reality – in fact the opposite of origami – where the folds eventually lead to a new three-dimensional shape being created from two-dimensional paper.

CARICACEAE: *Carica
papaya* Linnaeus,
Mexico, collected
by F. G. Meyer &
D. J. Rogers 2864,
1 August 1948

RHODOPHYTA:
*Batrachospermum
vagum* C. Agardh,
Guadeloupe, collected
by Monsieur Mazé,
28 September 1868

Latin is thought of as a dead language, no one speaks it, and its formalized, seemingly archaic rules are the bane of schoolchildren everywhere. But for botanists Latin is not a dead language, but is an essential part of the naming and describing of plants. All new species described must have a phrase telling the reader how this new species differs from all others like it – in Latin. The rest of the description can then be in any language, but botanists are bound to the Latin diagnosis by the rules that govern the naming of plants. Not only must new species have a Latin diagnosis, but most plant names are by convention derived from Latin or Greek. The simple reason for this is that Latin was the language of scholarship in the beginning of the scientific age. The father of modern plant taxonomy, Carolus Linneaus, whose *Species Plantarum* of 1753 was the first attempt to catalogue all known types of plants, used Latin and Greek roots and used many characters from mythology as plant names. *Nymphaea* – waterlilies – were named by Linnaeus for the water nymphs or nymphae. For many botanists a name was better if it in some way reflected the characteristics of the plant itself – thus the white waterlily is *Nymphaea alba*. Some names are very descriptive indeed. The freshwater alga here is called *Batrachospermum* in reference to its appearance. *Batrach* is the Greek root meaning frog and *spermum* the Latin word for seed. Putting these together gives us frog seed, or frog spawn – which perfectly describes the look of the gelatinous covering over a beaded dark interior. So perhaps Latin, instead of being dead and gone, is part of what gives botany its romance and excitement!

The orchid family is the most speciose on Earth. The fantastic and complex forms of orchid flowers have long fascinated people – and this comes as no surprise when one sees the flowers of *Dracula*. The name *Dracula* refers to the flower's resemblance to a small dragon (dracula means small dragon in Latin, the formal language of botany), not to Stoker's infamous vampire Count. The genus *Dracula* is composed of about 90 species of epiphytes, all of which have the same basic floral shape. The flowers are borne one at a time on a slender stalk, and have three, long-tailed sepals and three small petals. The sepals with their long thin tails are very conspicuous, but not only for their odd shape. Their colour is also unusual – in *D. roezlii*, the sepals are black or reddish-brown. The three creamy white petals are of basically two types. The lateral (or side) petals are very small, thick and stiff, while the lower petal or lip is of a most peculiar design. It is expanded, and looks exactly like the underside of a mushroom, complete with gills. It is easy to imagine the dragon now – the tailed blackish sepals are the elaborate head, the side petals the eyes and the lip the open mouth. But the apparently mysterious resemblance of the lip to a fungus does in fact have a function. The flowers of *Dracula* are visited by tiny flies, fungus gnats, who while attempting to lay eggs on the 'fungus' so beautifully set off by the black sepals, pollinate the plant. Too bad for the flies though, the orchid lip is not a good place to lay eggs. The duped flies go from flower to flower, wasting their precious next generation – so, to the flies at least, *Dracula* is as destructive as the vampire Count.

(To see the dragon, turn the plate upside-down.)

ORCHIDACEAE: *Dracula
roezlii* (Reichenbach.
f.) Luer, cultivated
from Colombia,
collected by
E. Shuttleworth,
October 1885

THEACEAE: *Camellia* x *williamsii* W.W. Smith (*C. japonica* Linnaeus x *C. saluenensis* Stapf) cultivar 'Philippa Forward', cultivated at the Hillier Arboretum, England, collected by the staff of the British Museum (Natural History) 1861, 1 May 1979

Few garden plants have as romantic a history as does the camellia. In the Orient, camellias have long been highly prized by emperors, shoguns, mandarins and samurai for their stylish beauty. They are used in the art and music of both China and Japan, and the species *Camellia sinensis*, the tea plant, has been cultivated for more than three thousand years. The camellia was brought to Europe on the spice ships of the Dutch and English East India companies. Slow to be appreciated as a garden plant due to its rarity, the popularity of the camellia peaked about 1860 – with the Victorian vogue for the more formal cultivars. The first dried material of these plants to reach Europe came from James Cunningham, a doctor stationed at Chusan on the Chinese island of Amoy at the end of the seventeenth century. Two ships a year were permitted trade with the Japanese, who under the rule of Iyemitsu adopted a policy of almost absolute exclusionism, which were often loaded with plants for trade. Living collections of camellias were established in England by 1732, and were known as Chinese rose. These first cultivated plants were the species *C. japonica*, a wild Japanese plant cultivated in China and thence brought to Britain. Later botanical exploration added many new species of *Camellia* to the horticultural trade – among them *C. saluenensis*. This species was collected by George Forrest in China between 1917 and 1925. Hybrids between this new species and the established *C. japonica* were raised by Mr J.C. Williams of Caerhays Castle, and the name of these hybrids *Camellia* x *williamsii* honours his contribution to horticulture.

When carnivorous plants are mentioned, the image that springs to mind is the Venus fly trap, snapping shut on some poor hapless fly or frog. But some carnivorous plants are subtle and discrete, while equally deadly for their victims. The genus *Utricularia*, or bladderworts, are the most ubiquitous of the carnivorous plants, and also the most inconspicuous. If they did not have showy yellow or purple flowers, they might well be overlooked by all but the professional plantfinder. These tiny, thread like plants have minute modified leaves – either on the above ground or underground stems – that are shaped like bladders, hence their common name. The bladders are the traps of *Utricularia*. The function of bladderwort traps has been the subject of research for more than a century and reads like a who's who of botany, with Charles Darwin one of the early investigators. Probably fooled by the small size of the trap itself, early botanists were reluctant to accept that the mechanism could be complex and rapid. The trap has a bulbous shape and near one end is a small opening surrounded by branched hairs. The opening, which has a thickened lower threshold, is guarded by two flaps of tissue, an upper hinged door, and a lower flap, the velum, which supports the door and keeps it shut when the trap is at rest. On the inside surface are small glands which during the resting stage absorb fluid from the interior of the bulbous trap. As a result of this absorption, the outside water pressure far exceeds that within the trap, and all is ready. The trap is sprung when a small animal brushes by one of the sensitive hairs at the opening. Stimulation of these hairs causes an electrical impulse which relaxes the velum – releasing the door to flip back into the interior of the trap. Under pressure, water rushes through the opening into the trap, sweeping the hapless victim with it. All this happens in 1/460th of a second – no wonder the early botanists didn't understand it! The door then closes when the water pressure is equalised and, since the door has a one way hinge, the prey item is trapped. The bladderwort then digests the prey item, and as water is absorbed by the glands, negative pressure is built up and the trap is ready for action again. Bladderworts trap many sorts of small aquatic insects, protozoans, water fleas and even have been found with small tadpoles in their traps. These larger animals don't fit in the trap, so they are digested a bit at a time, like a snake swallowing a large animal a bit at a time. *Utricularia* may be small, but to its victims, it is quite deadly!

LENTIBULARIACEAE: *Utricularia stellaris* Linnaeus, Zimbabwe, collected by E. L. Stephens 67, 23 July 1930

RHODOPHYTA:
Lemanea torulosa
C. Agardh, France,
collected by an
anonymous collector
around the turn of the
twentieth century

The alchemy of photosynthesis is part of what maintains life on Earth. Plants, by taking in carbon dioxide and turning it into oxygen and sugars provide us with the air we breathe and the food we eat. But plants also need oxygen to carry out respiration within their cells. Both respiration and photosynthesis usually take place in the light, and since photosynthesis rates far exceed those of respiration, the net effect is a release of oxygen into the atmosphere. Photosynthesis takes place inside the cells in tiny green organelles called chloroplasts. Their green colour is due to the presence of a specialised molecule – chlorophyll. When chlorophyll is struck by a photon, or packet of light, electrons of the pigment molecule become energised. These excited electrons are then eased down a gradient, losing energy along the way. The released energy is captured and used to synthesize ATP – the energy currency of all living things. Only those organisms that carry out photosynthesis can make ATP from energy-poor building blocks – the rest of us have to use up other energy-rich molecules to make ATP. Light energy is also used by plant cells to transfer hydrogen atoms from water to be used ultimately in the break up of carbon dioxide into oxygen and carbohydrates. Chlorophyll comes in several types, all of which perform more or less the same tasks. But other pigments in cells can also contribute to the photosynthetic process and in fact are essential to the algae many of which live at levels deep in the oceans where the light is weak and filtered. The tiny organelles where photosynthesis takes place are the remnants of an ancient association. Descended from once free-living organisms, they are in a permanent and symbiotic relationship with the cells that house them – a relationship that has been passed down through the generations. This symbiotic relationship may have occurred only once in the history of life, or perhaps many times – a question that remains to be solved.

Ocean currents have profound effects on both life in the sea, and life on land. The California Current brings cold water south from the North Pacific along the western coast of North America. This cold water supports a unique community of seaweeds, as well as the attendant animal life associated with them: sea otters, sea lions, and elephant seals. The graceful sea palm is only found in these cold waters, growing in treacherous conditions amid the roiling surf off exposed points of land. It resists the incessant forces of the waves with a combination of a strong holdfast (attachment point) and an incredibly flexible and resilient stalk. As the waves crash onto the sea palm, the stalk bends with the force, and as they recede, it regains its former stance unharmed! Competition for space is intense on these wave pounded points – mussels, barnacles and smaller algae all jockey for a secure position on the rocks. Most algae reproduce by releasing spores into the water – spores which may be sent drifting far and wide. The sea palm on the other hand needs a special mechanism for getting its younger generation established among the dangerous elements of its chosen home. While the tide is out, spores produced in special corrugated areas of the drooping fronds flow along these corrugations and drip onto the exposed rocks in enormous numbers. The spores attach immediately on the moist surfaces and begin to grow into tiny sea palms. If these tiny seaweeds do not get a good grip, they are washed away by the pounding waves and dispersed elsewhere – but they never compete well in areas occupied by other organisms. On exposed shores patches of open rock are constantly being opened up – a log crashing into a mussel bed, a patch of barnacles coming loose – providing an area for colonisation by sea palms. After reproduction and a year of being buffeted by the surf, the fronds of the sea palm fall off, leaving the elastic stalk behind to grow next year and begin the cycle again.

Flowers are usually thought of as symbols of purity and often innocence – we give them to each other as symbols of love on Valentine's Day and they have an attendant language all their own. But flowers are more important than our simple use of them – they are the plant's way of having sex. Sexual reproduction is extremely important for its role in maintaining genetic variability – only when two sets of chromosomes, one from a female and one from a male, come together do new combinations arise. Pollen is the plant equivalent of sperm, and ovules the plant equivalent of eggs. The goal for a plant is to get pollen from one individual to the ovules of another – this is pollination. Sounds simple, but it is certainly not. Plants must rely on something to carry pollen between individuals – they need 'borrowed mobility'. Pollen can be blown about by the wind, we all have suffered the agonies of hayfever when the spring grasses are reproducing! But more accurate methods usually involve animals as pollen vectors. This has led to partnerships in which there is an absolute mutual dependence of animal and plant. The biological function of flowers is to ensure that successful fertilisation happens and thus flower shape, size, colour and even scent can be thought of as advertising gimmicks to attract the right partner to transfer pollen. So why then should a flower smell and look like rotting flesh? But many do, and some of the most amazing are succulent members of the milkweed family growing in Africa. These large fleshy flowers, with their mottled patterns of brownish-purple and strong carrion smell, are pollinated by blowflies. These large flies lay eggs in rotting flesh where the maggots feed and aid in decomposition. The flies are attracted to the flowers by sight and smell, believing they are carrion. They then lay eggs near the centre of the flower and in the process get the bags of pollen produced by these plants attached to their bodies. The long thin hairs on the margins and surfaces of the flower are thought to attract the fly by either mimicking a swarm of other flies or a mass of seething maggots, indicating a good egg-laying site. Going to another flower to lay more eggs, they transfer pollen thus keeping their part of the 'bargain'. The flies definitely get the raw end of the deal though – as the maggots hatch they soon die from lack of food; although the flower looks like rotting meat, it is absolutely unsuitable as a food source for larval flies. The plant then has very effectively 'tricked' the fly into transferring pollen, without paying the price.

Palms epitomize the tropics. Whether rows of coconut palms gracing the beaches of islands in the South Pacific or a solitary individual left after deforestation in the Amazon, the image of a palm tree calls to mind sultry breezes and hot rainy climes. Palms have been called the most elegant of plants, and the epitome of what a plant should be. But palms are more than just an image to the peoples of the tropics – they represent shelter, food and sometimes a way of earning a living in an increasingly competitive world. The roof thatch used all over the tropics, in both the Old and New World, is usually composed of the leaves of palms. In any given area a particular species or set of species is preferred for thatch, and roofing from different types of palms can have a radically different appearance. Leaves are gathered one by one from the plants, and the palm itself is left to produce more leaves for the future – a truly renewable resource! Fruits of palms are important sources of fats, oils and vitamins in tropical parts of the world – the bright orange flesh in the fruit of the aguaje palm (*Mauritia flexuosa*) is one of the most vitamin A-rich foods in the world! Pejibaye (*Bactris gasipaes*) is cultivated on a large scale in Costa Rica and other Central American republics and the fruits are beginning to gain acceptance as a high value food source. But the fruits are not the only parts of the palm to provide food. The tender new growth leaf buds are harvested and sold as hearts of palm. One drawback to hearts of palm however is that in many species the plant must be killed to extract the heart. In the growing leaves, the heart, is found another true tropical delicacy – large beetle grubs, the size of a person's thumb, feed on the tender tissue. These grubs are much prized by local people and are an important source of fats – they are eaten alive as a trail-side snack and are quite delicious if you don't think too much about what you are eating! But palms also provide products that enable local people to earn cash – whether it be by selling vegetable ivory for the making of organic buttons or babussú oil for cooking. Palms are so much more than just an image of the tropics – in most tropical cultures they are truly the trees of life.

ARECACEAE:
Lepidocaryum tenue
Martius, Brazil,
collected by
J. W. H. Traill 1099,
31 January 1875

LEGUMINOSAE:
*Brownea rosa-
del-monte* Berg,
Panama, collected by
C. Whitefoord &
A. Eddy 513,
24 February 1982

Living collections of tropical plants were much prized in the early years of the exploration of both the New and Old World tropics. A dried specimen was essential for study by the academic botanists of the day, just as now, but horticulturists were covetous of the many spectacular finds sent back by early collectors. In the eighteenth century, while Linnaeus was actively working and revolutionising the study of botany, the spirit of the age was for the sponsorship of expeditions, preferably to the tropics for the express purpose of obtaining new taxa for the gardens of Europe. Nicolaus Joseph Jacquin was sent by Franz I, Emperor of Austria, to the Caribbean and northern South America with the specific assignment to collect as many plants as possible for the Schönbrunn Palace gardens. His taxonomic works published after his return were the first to use Linnaeus's new system of binomial nomenclature – when Linnaeus received his copy of the book in 1760 he 'could not sleep at night because I dreamed of your beautiful plants.' Jacquin named the spectacular *Brownea* in honour of Dr. Patrick Browne, an Irish naturalist who practised medicine in Jamaica and botanized extensively there. The genus soon became popular as a hothouse curiousity in Europe, arriving in England as early as 1793. However, it didn't flower until the mid-nineteenth century! But it was thought well worth waiting for by horticulturists, who coveted specimens of this 'magnificent object'. The introduction of plants from the tropics for hothouse cultivation was a tricky business. They were 'but sickly passengers at sea' and required constant care and attention on long ocean voyages. Efforts to bring back small tree seedlings or living plants rather than seeds often met with failure. Salt water is lethal to living plants, and any spray had to be washed off immediately. Constant temperature was maintained by the use of stoves, surely a fire risk on wooden sailing ships. The frequent storms brought hazards not only to the sailors aboard the ships, but also to their living cargo – growing plants were rooted in casks which were then bolted to the cabin floor. On fine days the casks and their inhabitants were brought to the deck to be exposed to the sun and the air, then carried back below at night. This represented an incredible amount of labour for members of an expedition already hard at work helping to sail the ship back to Europe. Seeing the magnificent rhododendron-like flowerhead of *Brownea* however, makes it easier to understand why the early explorers went to such great lengths to obtain living collections.

The plants and animals of islands have fascinated biologists since the first explorers found strange and peculiar creatures, such as dodos, moas and giant tortoises, on them. Islands are often havens of opportunity to the plants and animals that colonise them. Freed from competition and able to adapt to many different ways of life, many island organisms have undergone explosive adaptive radiation. Darwin's finches on the Galapagos, the silverswords of Hawaii (the genus *Argyroxiphium*), the birds of paradise of New Guinea, all these incredible examples of the diversity and splendour of life on earth have evolved on and are confined to islands. Islands are also rich in endemics – plants and animals occurring nowhere else. The isolation imposed by living on an island prevents interbreeding with other forms, thus over time leading to the development of distinct types of plants and animals – endemics. The group of volcanic archipelagos off the west coast of Africa are collectively known as Macaronesia and are composed of the Azores, Madeira, the Canaries and the Cape Verde Islands. Madeira, named for its cloak of forests by its discoverers, has long been referred to as paradise island. The profusion of plants that grow in its equable climate is justly famous, but more interesting to the botanists are the unique forms that are found only there. Some ten percent of the Madeiran flora is endemic, and certain genera, including *Teucrium*, have several endemic species on the island. The flora of Madeira was intensely studied in the nineteenth century by an English clergyman, Richard Thomas Lowe, and he published the first real account of plants of this island. His association with the Oxford High Church movement shocked Victorian England – ultimately resulting in Lowe's return to England. Leaving the island that was his home was profoundly depressing for him and he spent the rest of his life writing up his *Manual Flora of Madeira*. Today's botanists studying the plants of Madeira are indebted to Lowe for his painstaking observations and great love of this fascinating island flora, so rich in endemics.

LAMIACEAE: *Teucrium
betonicum* L'Héritier,
Madeira, collected by
J. R. Press 1018,
20 June 1985

PLATANACEAE: *Platanus mexicana* Moricand, Mexico, collected by M. Nee & K. Taylor 25785, 7 March 1983

Plane trees are a common sight on London streets. Their fast growth and remarkable tolerance of air pollution and compacted soil make them a popular street tree in many cities around the world. Their glossy leaves, easily washed clean of toxins by rain, and rapidly flaking bark contribute to their amazing ability to withstand pollution. The London plane, *Platanus* x *hispanica*, commonly cultivated as a street tree is a hybrid between the Oriental plane tree, *Platanus orientalis* from China, and the American plane tree, *Platanus occidentalis* from North America and Mexico. This hybrid was in cultivation in England by at least the middle of the eighteenth century, but its exact origins are obscure. Its great vigour and extreme variability have both been attributed to its hybrid status. Plane trees, called sycamores in the United States, have their flowers in small globose heads with each head being either male or female. In Mexico, where the common plane is *Platanus mexicana*, the trees grow along the banks of rivers and streams, where the wind and water distribute their plumed seeds. The family Platanacaceae is completely restricted to the Northern Hemisphere and its distribution is typical of those groups that originated on the super continent Laurasia, which broke up over time to become present-day North America and Eurasia. The history of the Earth has profoundly influenced the distribution and evolution of plants and animals on its surface, and many enigmatic problems in biogeography can be solved by investigating the past.

Coffee is one of the most ubiquitous drugs in use today. Before the advent of tea, whose cultivation began on a major scale in the nineteenth century, coffee was drunk both morning and evening. The coffee-tree, *Coffea arabica*, is native to the mountains of Africa, but is now grown around the world. The family to which coffee belongs is the Rubiaceae, which contains some real surprises, plants one would have never thought were related to our daily drink. The anti-malarial drug that allowed the British to colonise the tropics – quinine – comes from the cinchona tree, a member of the coffee family. Without quinine Europeans died like flies from malaria in the tropics. The plant was native to the Andean region, controlled by the Spanish crown, and until the British established plantations of cinchona in their own colonies in South East Asia, they were dependent upon trade with Spain for the drug. Ipecac, a potent purgative and emetic, comes from *Cephaelis ipecahuanha*, another tropical member of the family. Gardenias, the most fragrant of greenhouse shrubs, are related to coffee – and if you look carefully at the leaves you can see why. Most members of the coffee family have opposite leaves with a pair of leaf-like organs at their bases. These stipules are usually fused together and often have quite amazing shapes and forms. In the bedstraws, common herbs of our northern hedgerows and meadows, the stipules are the size and shape of the leaves, giving each node (the point at which the leaves arise) the appearance of a wheel. Bedstraws are so named for their use in mattresses, but some say the name comes from their supposed use as one of the cradle herbs in the manger at Bethlehem. Bedstraws are members of the genus *Galium*, which was also of great medicinal importance in the past. Various species were used for skin complaints, cancers and as a general tonic, and sweet woodruff was used in Germany as a component of *Maibowle*, a drink for the celebration of spring. Whether as medicines, enjoyable stimulants or as horticultural wonders, members of the coffee family, the Rubiaceae, are of undisputed use to a wide variety of human societies.

RUBIACEAE: *Galium philippinense* Merrill, Philippines, collected by J. K. Santos, April-June 1918

SCHIZAEACEAE:
Lygodium palmatum
(Bernhardi) Swartz,
United States,
provenance unknown.

Ferns are among the most recognisable of plants – their graceful feathery fronds are present in the shade of forests world-wide. Ferns, however, are an amazingly large and diverse group of plants as well as being the epitome of grace and beauty. They are found from sea level to the highest mountains, and in all habitats from wet rain forests to arid deserts. Ferns are non-flowering plants, and the absence of flowers on ferns has been explained in some extraordinary ways. They were once thought to bear minute, very short-lived flowers open and fertile only on mid-summer's eve – which then as they matured, produced tiny dust-like seeds. 'Seeds' of the male fern were thought to render a person invisible! These 'seeds' are in fact spores and are an essential part of the reproductive cycle of ferns, but it was not until the eighteenth century that the complexity of fern reproduction was explained in full. Spores are either borne in special pouches or under umbrella-like structures called sori on the undersides of all fronds, or are only borne on quite different looking fertile fronds – as in the tropical climbing fern *Lygodium*. Spores in ferns are not really the equivalent of seeds as they germinate to form gametophytes – the haploid generation which has a single set of chromosomes. On this small, usually heart-shaped pad of tissue develop the sex organs of the fern. From the male sex organs (antheridia) sperm are released. The sperm swim through a film of water to reach the female sex organs (archegonia) and fertilisation takes place. The tiny fern, now with its full two sets of chromosomes, then grows out from the parent gametophyte – ultimately becoming the graceful plant we all recognise. This alternation of generations – between haploid and diploid phases – is characteristic of all plants. In the non-flowering plants, such as ferns, the two phases are both free-living, as gametophyte and sporophyte, while in the flowering plants, the haploid phase, the gametophyte, is always contained within the larger, free-living sporophyte.

Gentians are the quintessential alpine plants – tiny and delicate, with beautiful flowers. They are primarily montane in origin and have become emblematic of all mountain floras. The genus *Gentiana* has a very wide range, with species occurring on all the major continents, but the real diversity in the genus is found in Asia. China alone has some 248 species, nearly two-thirds of the world's total. The flowers of gentians are always tubular and vary in colour from yellow, to reddish purple to white. But it is the almost unbelievable blues of those species with blue flowers that so capture the imagination. Nowhere else in the plant world are such striking blues encountered. Of all garden plants, alpines certainly are the ones owing most to plant hunters. We cultivate mainly species of alpines, rarely is there the urge to hybridise and improve – in fact, rare and unusual species are actively sought after as pure lines. Gentians were first cultivated in England sometime in the sixteenth century, and were quite well known from many parts of the world by the nineteenth century. Many of the more commonly cultivated garden species have come from Asia – *G. sino-ornata* from Yunnan, *G. farreri* introduced by Mr Farrer from Kansu, *G. gilvostriata* brought by Capt. Kingdon-Ward from the Burmese-Tibetan frontier – the list is long and reads like a biography of plant exploration. But Europe has its own native gentian species too. The serried ranks of tiny plants on this herbarium specimen of *Gentiana pumila* – each one an individual plant – recall an army marching across the page. This exquisite miniature with its azure blue flowers grows in tufts among the stones and short turf in the limestone formations of the Southeastern Alps. Difficult to grow in the greenhouse, its glowing jewel-like beauty has been much appreciated in its native habitat by generations of botanists and botanical tourists.

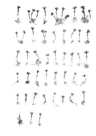

GENTIANACEAE:
Gentiana pumila
Jacquin, Italian Alps,
collected by
W. C. Barton,
13 August 1928

CYPERACEAE: *Carex vesicaria* Linnaeus, British Isles, collected by C. E. Salmon, 7 June 1903

'Sedges have edges and rushes are round' is a doggerel rhyme learned by many beginning botany students as the way to distinguish two very similar plant families. The edges referred to are those on the stem – most sedges have a three-angled stem, while the stems of rushes (and grasses) are round and smooth. Sedges, rushes and grasses all are grass-like plants with narrow, parallel-veined leaves and compact groups of tiny greenish or brownish flowers. Grasses are often thought of as a nuisance – hay-fever in the spring, and the seemingly endless lawn-mowing of summer. But in fact grasses are the staff of life – wheat, maize, rye, millet, barley, sorghum and rice are all grasses. Many of the world's great civilisations have grown up around a cultivated grass staple – the Incas of the South American Andes, who depended upon the potato, are one of the few exceptions. The grain we use is the seed of the grass plant – containing starchy endosperm, the nutritive tissue of the seed, and a protein-rich embryo. The ability to cultivate and harvest such high quality food sources has had a profound effect on the development of human civilisation and culture. The impact of grasses has been on the nutrition of our species, but sedges have had another, perhaps equally, important role. The papyrus reed is a sedge – in the genus *Cyperus*. Papyrus was first used to make paper by the scribes of the Nile Valley kingdoms some 5000 years ago. Then, as now, information is power, and the scribes with their complex and accurate records of taxes, harvest and laws certainly had the information! The development of paper-making technology revolutionised the way in which information was disseminated and stored, making the large libraries of the ancient world possible. Written records have played a vital part in almost every civilisation since the Egyptians and some feel that writing is of such importance that human society could not exist without it. Communication is part of what makes us human, and the ability to keep records and pass them from generation to generation has greatly speeded up our social and cultural evolution. Such seemingly insignificant plants, grasses and sedges, provide two of the essential components of our society, the bread we eat and the paper we write upon.

Naturally occurring variation in flower colour has been exploited by plant breeders in creating the riot of colours we plant in our gardens every year. Every gardener or walker has seen a white bluebell or forget-me-not, and many plants display a very wide range of colours. Charles Darwin, the father of today's science of evolutionary biology, experimented widely with plants in his garden. He drew analogies between the methodical selective procedures practised by plant and animal breeders and the process of natural selection by which organic diversity is generated and maintained. His meticulous crosses of colour forms of plants – snapdragons, stocks, sweet-peas – led him to observe that some characters refused to blend in offspring. Prevailing wisdom at the time was that interbreeding caused a blending of characteristics – these characteristics of organisms were caused by 'organic atoms of nature'. The free intercrossing of different forms or variations would ultimately result in the homogenisation or complete blending of those forms, were not natural selection acting upon them. In another part of Europe, at about the same time, the mid-nineteenth century, the modest monk Father Gregor Mendel was performing the same sorts of crossing experiments on garden peas in his garden. He however, methodically kept track of the ratios of colour (and other) variations in the offspring, and in the process discovered a new way of looking at the phenomenon we now call genetic inheritance. His precise and quantitative information on the degree to which characters do or do not blend in the offspring, and the repeatability of his results heralded the science we now call genetics – now a multimillion dollar research industry, as complete with the attendant benefits and potential dangers as nuclear power was in the 1950s.

RANUNCULACEAE: *Anemone pavonina* Lamarck, cultivated in Sussex, England, collected by C. C. Lacaita, 15 May 1922

MELASTOMATACEAE:
Clidemia octona
(Bonpland) L. Jussieu,
Belize, collected by
J. N. Hedger 36,
21 July 1966

Veins are the plumbing of a leaf. Veins themselves are tubular structures, whose walls are re-enforced with lignin, the same substance that makes wood. It is through the stiffened veins that water flows to all the cells of the leaf and that sugars manufactured during photosynthesis are distributed to the rest of the plant. Veins begin large, divide and divide again, like our own blood vessels – so that tiny veinlets, like our own capillaries, reach every part of the leaf. Just how ramified this network is can be easily seen in the delicate ghost-like 'skeletons' of leaves decomposing on the forest floor. The patterns of venation in leaves are incredibly varied – from the strictly parallel veins of a grass leaf to the complex net-like pattern in a fig leaf. Paleobotanists, botanists studying fossil plants, often have only the vein patterns to go on as clues to the identity of a fossil leaf since the fabric of the leaf is destroyed in the fossilisation process, just as it is during decomposition. Some plant families can even be identified solely on the basis of their leaf venation. The tropical family Melastomataceae is one of these. Members of this family have leaves with three to five strongly parallel main veins that look like the elongate fingers of a hand. Between these main veins run sets of veins like the rungs of a ladder – creating an unmistakable pattern. Since in the rain forest many plants are not in bloom most of the time, clues as to their identity using such leaf characteristics are essential.

Bark is the outermost covering of woody stems and protects the growing tissue underneath. Bark can be a very important characteristic used to tell tree species apart – and its variety and beauty is quite tremendous. Birch trees, for example, all have very distinctive, thin, often peeling bark. It usually has large, horizontal lenticels which look like darker stripes scattered at random over the tree trunk. Lenticels are the pores of the bark – it is through them that gas exchange takes place, a process essential for the life of the tree. The uses of bark by people are many and varied – quinine, used to treat malaria, comes from an extract of the bark of the chinchona tree and the corks in our wine bottles are made from the bark of the cork oak. One of the most famous uses for birch bark – and one of the most spectacular uses for bark anywhere – is in the construction of canoes. Various peoples around the world have used bark for making boats of one kind or another, but the skill of the native peoples of North America was unsurpassed. Early travellers to North America were amazed by the lightweight, extremely quick-moving water craft used by native peoples they encountered. The frames of these canoes were built from a variety of woods, but the coverings were always of birch bark – peeled in large sheets from carefully selected trees. The bark was peeled from the tree in such a way as not to harm the growing layer underneath, and in time a new bark layer grew back. The original craft used by native peoples were small and agile, but they later made much larger canoes for use by fur traders in the region. Some of these were up to 11 metres long and could carry loads of up to four thousand kilograms! Different tribal groups had different styles of canoes, but all were light and easy to manoeuvre. Birch bark was also used in North America for all kinds of utensils and containers, allowing for a highly mobile society able to live in harmony with the environment.

BETUALCEAE: *Betula albo-sinensis* Burkill, China, collected by Rev. Fr. Hugh, July 1899

To be useful for future generations of scientists, a plant, both the specimen and its name, needs to be uniquely identifiable. The careful and systematic recording of collection data is essential – labels that say a plant was collected in the New World, so common only a few centuries ago, will no longer do. By tradition, a collector keeps track of his or her plants with a system of consecutive numbers beginning, not surprisingly, with 1. The specimen here is the thirty-eight thousand seven hundred and ninety-seventh different plant collected by this botanist. Early collectors often did not use a consecutive numbering system – instead relying on the identity of the plants as a distinguishing factor. Thus the potential existed for many mix-ups to be made with these plants. In the eighteenth century, when plants were flooding European botanical gardens from all over the world, plants from China were labelled as from Peru and many mysteries of plant origins can be traced to similar inaccuracies of keeping track of collections. The unique combination of collector's name and collecting number means that all people using the specimen can be sure they are referring to the same thing. But, as with all fool-proof systems, things can go wrong. The collector can mix things up by collecting more than one plant under a single number, or a label can be placed on the wrong plant during preparation and storage of the specimen. These cases however are easily correctable, unlike the mix-ups of yester-year. The scientific name of the plant too must be uniquely identifiable – the 'Vahl' in the scientific name of this specimen refers to Martin Vahl, a Danish botanist who named the species to which this specimen belongs in the early seventeenth century. This differentiates it from any other 'Utricularia juncea' – we all know it is Vahl's name we mean. The careful keeping track of both names and specimens makes it possible for taxonomists to pursue their trade, and is the basis for the common language of botany.

When we think of the first domesticated plants, we think of the main staples, wheat, maize, rice. But other important components of our diet have equally long and complex histories. Origins of the cultivated onions are shrouded in mystery, but one thing is certain – they have been with us for a very long time. Garlic and onions have both been found in archaeological sites in the Dead Sea region from 3500 BC and two thirds of the types of garlic cultivated today were already in cultivation at the time of the Roman philosopher and natural historian Pliny in the first century AD. Onions were one of the most popular crops in ancient Egypt, and when the Israelites complained about hardships on their journey with Moses to the Promised Land, they remembered the good food they had as slaves – 'and the leeks, and the onions, and the garlick'. Onions accompanied the dead to the other world – Egyptian mummies have often been found with onions in the body cavities, against the face, on the chest or attached to the soles of the feet. Not only were onions and their relatives a valued food, they were also widely used as a medicine from India to Greece. They had both beneficial and detrimental effects – on the plus side, onions were said to have diuretic properties, be good for the digestive tract and the eyes, to act as a heart stimulant, and to be useful as a cure for rheumatism. Garlic is known to be a powerful bactericide and is a much-used charm against evil spirits. On the minus side, onions were looked down upon in India as a food inappropriate for those pursuing a spiritual life – probably as a result of their strong odour and stimulant properties. In Elizabethan times, John Gerard felt that onions caused windiness and over-sleepiness, especially if eaten raw. At present the consumption of garlic is thought to be one of the reasons for the low incidence of heart disease in the Mediterranean countries relative to northern Europe. The cultivated onions are not all derived from one species, there are at least seven species involved. Leeks are *Allium ampeloprasum*, as the national symbol of Wales, they commemorate the victory of Cadwaller over the Saxons in 640 AD. Onions, shallots and tree onions are *Allium cepa*, while the garlics are *Allium sativum*. The chives are *Allium schoenoprasum* and several less well-known species are cultivated in various parts of the world, and many wild species are used by native peoples in Europe and North America. The ubiquity with which members of the onion family are used by human societies merely serves to underline the fact that food has always been a pleasure as well as a necessity.

LENTIBULARIACEAE:
Utricularia juncea
Vahl, Honduras,
collected by
G. R. Proctor 38797, 31
January 1981

AMARYLLIDACEAE:
Allium fistulosum
Linnaeus, cultivated,
from the herbarium
of P. S. Pallas, late
eighteenth century

THEACEAE: *Camellia saluenensis* Stapf, cultivated at the Hillier Arboretum, England, collected by the staff of the British Museum (Natural History) 1396, 25 April 1978

Tea is always associated with Great Britain and is intimately linked with the expansion of the British Empire. Yet who, while drinking a cup of tea, stops to consider the strange history of its origins? Tea has become so bound up with the British way of life that it has become commonplace – but the story of tea, as with the stories of many of our most useful plants, is full of romance and controversy. The tea plant is a camellia, perhaps more familiar to us as a flowering garden shrub, growing to three or four metres tall in the rainforests of Southeast Asia. Tea has been cultivated in China and adjacent Southeast Asia for more than 2000 years, usually in small plots by individual farmers. How people discovered that the first new leaves of this plant could be processed and infused to make a palatable drink is cloaked in mystery. Perhaps as is commonly believed the drink was first used as a medicine and only later became a beverage of choice. China began trading tea with the outside world in the tenth and eleventh centuries, but it only began to reach Europe in the seventeenth century. The first tea to come to England came via the Dutch and it was first served in public in 1657. In the late seventeenth century the English East Indian Company gained a monopoly on the tea trade with China, and by the 1860s tea-clippers, fast sailing ships of which the *Cutty Sark* is one of the last remaining, brought the crop from China to the London docks in 90 days. But the days of China tea were numbered. What happened next is cloaked in mystery – some maintaining that a native variety of tea was discovered in India, others maintaining that it had been introduced secretly and illegally to Assam from China by the East India Company. Exactly how tea got to Assam is no longer important and will probably remain a mystery, but the result of its presence was the development of Empire tea production. By 1887 England imported more tea from India and Sri Lanka than from China and the newly developed method of plantation cultivation in India meant that the Chinese could no longer compete. From then on, tea and the British Empire became intimately linked. By 1900 more than a million acres of tropical rainforest had been felled in British India and Ceylon and planted up with tea to satisfy the home market. The environmental cost was tremendous as was the human cost – planters literally carved their estates out of the jungle and overcame great hardship to achieve their goals. Plants used by humans are our greatest resource; they feed us, clothe us and are completely renewable. Often those plants most useful to us however have their origins cloaked in mystery – we have spent so many generations changing them to suit our needs that they no longer exist in a truly wild form.

Since antiquity, roses have been associated with goddesses of love, their passions and the search for perfection in beauty. Aphrodite's flower was the rose – said to have been created by the earth in her honour as she was born from the ocean. Rose-wreathed Isis, the Egyptian goddess of love, and her son Horus are said to have been absorbed into the emerging Christian faith of the first centuries AD as the Madonna and Child – a potent symbol of mother-love and of divine effect. The Virgin of Guadelupe – the first vision of the Madonna as a dark-skinned native of the New World – was seen by a peasant near Mexico City. She filled his simple peasant cloak with roses several times, and finally his cloak was imprinted with the image of Mary standing on a half moon, rising from a cloud of roses. Thus was the love of God for the newly conquered peoples of Mexico symbolised. Thousands still flock to the shrine in Mexico, crawling on their knees for miles and miles. Love, sweet as it is, is often however accompanied by suffering and even by pain – as the exquisite flower of the rose is accompanied by vicious thorny stems. In Greek mythology, red roses were created as Aphrodite's bleeding feet stained the delicate white flowers of the thorny rose when she rushed to the aid of her lover Adonis, murdered by her jealous husband. Or perhaps Eve's lips on the first roses in the Garden of Eden caused the flower to blush – creating the first red rose! The crown of thorns worn by Jesus as he was crucified was said to have been fashioned from briar rose stems, and from drops of his blood the first red rose bushes grew. The pagan associations with roses – goddesses, lovers and intense passion – were disapproved of by the early Christian church, and so roses were banned from use in Christian burials. But they continued to spring, apparently unaided, from graves everywhere and so ultimately the church gave up its fruitless opposition and adopted the rose as a symbol of Christian purity and martyrdom. However, roses blooming out of season, roses dropping their leaves or petals, or more ominously a dream about a white rose are all still omens of death. In contrast, white roses are planted on a virgin's grave as a symbol of purity. In death, as in life, love reigns supreme, with all its joy and suffering. Roses too remain a symbol of love's power – and a multi-million industry every February for Valentine's Day.

ROSACEAE: *Rosa parvifolia* Willdenow, cultivated, from the herbarium of J. J. Roemer, 1763-1819

LILIACEAE: *Gloriosa verschuurii* T.M. Hoog, cultivated at RHS Gardens, Wisley, collected by Wm. T. Stearn s.n., 26 July 1954

The study of animal behaviour is well-documented on our television screens and in magazine articles, but the private lives of plants are much more elusive and require patience to observe and enjoy. One very obvious way in which plants 'behave' is in their movements. That plants move is without doubt – the time scale is just so slow that we rarely witness the action itself. Some movement is towards the light, but other plant movement is in response to the stimulus of touch. It seems odd to think of plants as having a 'sense of touch', but many of the vining and climbing plants respond to contact with differential growth. Plants climb by a variety of methods, but these can be divided into three basic types: scrambling, twining and by the use of tendrils. Scramblers attach themselves to other objects by hooks, spines or barbs, while twiners coil their stem around the support. It is in plants with tendrils that the coiling reaction is in response to contact – these are the plants with a sense of touch! Tendrils are amazingly variable, they can be derived from many different parts of the plant – from stems, as in the grapes, from roots, as in vanilla orchids, from leaflets, as in the garden pea, from leaf stalks, as in clematis, and even from the tips of leaves themselves, as in the gloriosa lily. Young tendrils move in a random way, as if searching for an appropriate support onto which they might attach. These movements are wide sweeping ones and appear to involve changes in pressure within the cells. When the tendril makes contact with a support, what is called contact coiling begins and firmly attaches the climbing plant to the support. This coiling is the result of different rates of growth on the two sides of the tendril and can be stimulated just by stroking the tendril in the laboratory! After the climber is firmly attached to its support, free coiling begins, drawing it closer to the support and setting the tendril up to act as a spring-like buffer against the forces of the wind. Within the coiled tendril, supporting tissue is laid down – in some species a single tendril can support a half a kilogram of weight! This is truly behaviour – it has phases, it is in direct response to a stimulus, and we can observe it. Plants lead secret lives indeed, but at their own, relatively slow pace. It needs only patience to really see what they get up to.

The mystery and romance of China and the Far East has long held Europeans in its sway. One of the earliest authoritative accounts of the Far East by a European was that of the famous explorer Marco Polo, who travelled to China in the early thirteenth century. His father and uncle were Venetian traders, and in 1260 they made a journey taking them from what is now Uzbekistan to China and the court of the Emperor Kublai Khan. Upon their return they set out again for China, this time accompanied by the young Marco. It took them four years to travel overland from present day Israel, northwards through Iran, and across the Gobi desert to reach the court of Kublai Khan, then in Shang-tu. They were the first Europeans to reach these parts of the Far East, and they must have seemed as exotic to the Chinese as the Chinese seemed to them. The traders stayed in China and Marco joined the Kublai Khan's diplomatic service, acting as his agent on missions to many parts of the far-flung Empire. He and his father and uncle served Kublai Khan for almost twenty years, only returning to Venice after escorting a Mongol princess by sea to Iran, thereby visiting many previously unexplored parts of Southeast Asia as well. Marco Polo became a soldier once back in Venice, and while captaining a Venetian ship in a battle between the city states of Genoa and Venice, was taken prisoner. During his imprisonment in Genoa he dictated a detailed account of his travels to a fellow prisoner. Thus the most famous and influential travel book in history was born – *The Travels of Marco Polo*. The book became the basis for the first accurate maps of the Far East and was the inspiration for the voyages of Christopher Columbus, who in trying to reach the Orient by going west discovered the New World by accident. Whilst travelling throughout China, Marco Polo observed many uses for the plants of the region – not only for spices but for a multitude of other purposes as well. But surprisingly one plant he never records the use of is tea. Tea drinking had been recorded from China more than four centuries earlier by Arab merchants visiting during the ninth century. Perhaps Marco Polo, remembering and dictating in prison, was so acculturated to the Chinese way of life that while other plants were special and worthy of mention, tea was merely part of the background.

RUBIACEAE: *Nertera sinensis* Hemsley, China, collected by the Sino-American Guizhou Botanical Expedition 2002, 5-9 October 1986

CACTACEAE:
*Echinocereus
engelmannii* (Parry)
Rumple, California,
collected by E. K. Balls
11564, 12 May 1958

The flowers of cacti are as beautiful as the plants are vegetatively peculiar. The brilliant yellows and especially the fantastic magentas that one sees in cacti flowers are due to the prescence of a class of chemicals found only in the cacti and a small group of related plant families. Most of the red coloration in flowers comes from pigments called anthocyananins. But in the cacti and their relatives (including beetroots and iceplants) a very different sort of compound is involved. Nitrogen is found in the green pigments of leaves, the chlorophylls, but is very uncommon in flower pigments. The peculiar red pigments of cacti and their relatives do however contain nitrogen, which led in part to the discovery of these pigments. That the pigments in the roots of beets were different from those in roses and geraniums was known as long ago as the 1800s, but the discovery of just how different these chemicals are structurally was only made in the 1960s. In the nineteenth century red wines were commonly adulterated with beetroot or pokeberry (*Phytolacca*) juice, enhancing and deepening their colour. The need for accurate identification of these contaminants prompted the development of chemical tests to detect them. Colour tests were used to detect the betanins, as they were called, until the 1950s. The nineteenth century chemists discovered that crude preparations of the pigment contained up to seven percent nitrogen, but did not have the technology with which to elucidate the profound structural differences between the betanins and the more common anthocyanins. In addition to detecting these pigments as 'wine enhancers', nineteenth century botanists realised that they might be useful in determining relationships amongst families of plants. Plants of the order 'Centrospermae' (meaning seeds in the middle – referring to the central placenta in the ovary) all seemed to contain these compounds and completely lack anthocyanins, providing added evidence as to the closeness of their relationship. Today's botanists still group these plants together, and the possession of this unique class of nitrogenous pigments, the betalains, is one of the pieces of evidence that allows us to make hypotheses about the evolutionary past.

'The mind is a chaos of delight...' was how Charles Darwin described his reactions to the splendour of his first sight of the Brazilian rain forest. The mysterious order in chaos is apparent every day in the patterns we see in living things. The apparently haphazard profusions of nature are intensely pleasing to many people, as they were to Darwin when he stepped off the Beagle onto South American soil. For a long time, the underlying order of such apparent chaos escaped notice and explanation. Living things are what scientists studying chaos call dynamical systems – composed of so many interacting elements that they are sensitive to the tiniest change. In such systems very slight differences in starting points cause very profound differences in endpoints. Chaos theory tells the story of the many paths taken by dynamical systems as they change over time, while fractal geometry records their movements in space. We see fractals all the time, every day. The branching structure of the fern is a perfect example. As a fern frond unrolls, each tiny division unrolls in a similar way, and each tiny division shows similar details on a different scale. As we look more closely at the fern frond, we see that the shapes seen at one scale are very similar to those seen at a smaller scale. This self-similarity is characteristic of the tangled dimensions of fractal geometry. A closer look at many plants and animals will reveal their fractal structure, and the constantly changing world endlessly creates new opportunities for evolution by natural selection to work upon. Some even feel that the old concept of the balance of nature, with everything in its place and a place for everything, is giving way to a more dynamic, ever-changing and wonderfully diverse chaos of nature.

DENNSTAEDTIACEAE:
Dennstaedtia hooveri
Christ, Philippines,
collected by
E. B. Copeland 188,
May 1917

IRIDACEAE: *Crocus balansae* Gay, Turkey, collected by G. Maw 322, in Turkey on 1 May 1877, the specimen taken from plants grown in the gardens of Benthall Hall and collected on 12 February 1878.

Carl Linnaeus completely transformed the science of botany. Son of a Lutheran curate, Linnaeus was born in Sweden in the first years of the eighteenth century and grew up surrounded by plants and flowers, as his father was a keen gardener and something of a botanist. He made his way, not without difficulty, through university and was trained as a physician. He practised medicine on and off throughout his early career, but in 1741 he was appointed the professor of medicine and botany at Uppsala University where he was to remain for the rest of his life. Linnaeus formulated rules, or aphorisms, of botany and the orderliness of his thinking has had a profound influence on science to this day. The publication of his *Species Plantarum*, a summary of the distinguishing features of all of the then known plant species, in 1753, marks the most significant turning point in how we name and refer to plants today. Prior to the publication of *Species Plantarum* botanists referred to species of plants using long Latin polynomials or phrase names, the first word of which was the genus. Linneaus also referred to the species of plants in this way, but he introduced a system of what he called trivial names – single word designations that in combination with the genus could serve as a sort of shorthand for the longer, more complicated phrase names. These trivial names could be a single word, taken freely from anywhere – and the task of coining them for all 5900 species treated in *Species Plantarum* left Linnaeus exhausted. But their use certainly changed the way plants were named and remembered! The 'trivial' combination *Crocus sativus*, used in 1753, is certainly easier to remember and refer to than *Crocus spatha univalvi radicali, corollae tubo longissimo*, its Linnaean phrase name. This somewhat accidental system of binomial nomenclature (naming with two words) caught on – and it is still in use today. Botanists have completely abandoned the phrase name altogether. Scientific names now consist of two basic parts – the generic name and the specific epithet which corresponds to Linnaeus's trivial name. Linnaeus never intended to revolutionise botany – but all botanists today use *Species Plantarum* as the starting point for the naming of plants and we all use his elegant system of trivial names.

A million stigmas are hand-harvested to make ten kilos of saffron – a spice truely worth its weight in gold. The bright yellow colour and pungent, aromatic scent of saffron were much prized by the peoples of the Middle East. Spices and flavourings are often made from the leaves or seeds of plants, but saffron is unique in being made from dried stigmas – the surface on which pollen grains fall to fertilise ovules to make seeds. Unlike the common crocuses, which we all know as the harbingers of spring, the saffron crocus flowers in the autumn, with the leaves. The stigmas of the flowers of *Crocus sativus* are large and bright orange-yellow, and to make saffron each is hand-picked from the flower and then dried on a kiln between two layers of paper under pressure from thick boards. The result is a bright yellow cake. The average yield from an acre of crocuses in the first year after planting is a little less than a kilo, but for two years after that the same field will yield some ten kilos of the dried product. About 4,500 flowers are required to yield one ounce of dried, powdered saffron! Saffron was one of the 'chief spices' detailed in the Song of Solomon and was prized by the Hebrews, Greeks and Romans not only as a spice, but also as a dye. Saffron yellow shoes were worn only by royalty in ancient Persia, and Greek gods, goddesses, nymphs and vestal virgins were said to be dressed in saffron robes. The saffron crocus was introduced to Spain by the Arabs as a trade article and its modern English name is derived from the Arabic *zaffer*, as is the Spanish common name, azafrán. *Crocus sativus* was imported into England in ancient times, and for a time, England became a centre for trade in the spice. Towns like Saffron Walden in Essex were centres for the cultivation of the plants and presumably places like Saffron Hill in London were export hubs. Now however, saffron cultivation in England exists only as a memory, preserved in place names and traditional recipes.

IRIDACEAE: *Crocus corsicus* Vanucci, cultivated in England from plants from Corsica, collected by J. Shaw, April 1875

RUBIACEAE:
*Warszewiczia
coccinea* (Vahl)
Klotsch, Panama,
collected by C. White-
foord & A. Eddy 511,
20 February 1982

Most people think of the tropical rainforest as a riot of colour, with brightly coloured flowers and fantastic wild animals everywhere. The reality is a little bit more prosaic: in fact, colour is very difficult to find. Green, in many shades to be sure, but still a single colour, is the dominant colour in the rainforest. In this monochrome sea of green, splashes of other colours are startling and attract the attention of not only the occasional passing human being, but more importantly, the animals of the forest. The brilliant red colour of the inflorescence of the sanguinaria tree (*Warszewiczia coccinea*) is like a flag advertising the riches within. In this plant, the flowers themselves are not especially attractive – they are small and brownish orange – and another part of the plant has taken over the function of advertising. In *Warszewiczia*, the flowers are grouped in clusters along the axis of the inflorescence. One flower in each cluster has just one of its calyx lobes hugely expanded and almost leaf-like in appearance but of a brilliant, blood red colour which is highly visible in the otherwise green environment, especially with the sun on it. This attracts hummingbirds and butterflies by the dozen to the plant where they find, in the tiny drab flowers, rich nectar resources. Some butterflies even learn the locations of individual sanguinaria trees in their territories and come back to them day after day, finding new flowers with fresh nectar each day in the long-lived inflorescences. The single brilliantly coloured flag serves as an advertising billboard for the whole flower cluster over its entire life-span. But this is not a one way interaction with butterflies and hummingbirds getting energy in the form of nectar for free. While probing in the flowers and sucking up the sweet liquid the flower visitors rub against the stamens or the flower and get a dusting of pollen on their bodies or heads. When they visit subsequent flowers, perhaps on a different tree some distance away, the pollen comes into contact with the stigma and bingo, fertilisation occurs! So every partner in this interaction benefits – the insect or bird gets energy in the form of sugar rich nectar, and the plant gets pollen transferred from one flower to another. Both partners use their benefits to the same ultimate end – reproduction of more like themselves.

Tropical rainforests are dynamic living systems – not static cathedral-like repositories of the diversity of life on earth. Large forest giants fall, leaving great holes in the canopy, letting the light stream in. This increase in light, heat and open space in which to grow starts off the process known as secondary succession, an important factor in the maintenance of diversity in the tropics. Certain fast-growing plants are the first to invade areas opened up by treefalls or landslides – or more recently and much more widely, by human disturbance due to logging, farming or clear-cutting. Cecropias are common in such gaps all over the Neotropics. The seeds of guarumo, as the genus *Cecropia* is known all over Spanish-speaking Latin America, persist in the soil between episodes of disturbance and burst into action when light and heat levels rise following a landslide or a treefall. The seedlings grow very quickly and the large leaves effectively trap the incoming sunlight, often preventing it from reaching other, more slowly growing plants. The trees grow to medium height, about ten metres or so, and have very light, soft wood. *Cecropia* trees are in almost continuous flower and fruit and produce huge quantities of seed which is dispersed, often far away from the parent plant, by bats. Plants like *Cecropia* are known as pioneers and most have similar characteristics – balsa wood used for the manufacture of model aeroplanes comes from another neotropical pioneer species. As the pioneers in a disturbed area grow up, less light reaches the forest floor and the competition for available light and nutrients increases. Seedlings of species of forest trees, that are able to germinate in the shade, can now begin to thrive. The pioneer trees are less able to compete for space in the changed habitat, and the succession moves on. Pioneer species are found in low densities throughout the forest, but it is when a disturbance occurs that they explode into action!

CECROPIACEAE:
Cecropia scheberiana
Miquel, Dominica,
collected by
G. A. Ramage,
24 June 1888

UMBELLIFERAE:
Angelica cyclocarpa
(C. Norman) Cannon,
Nepal, collected by
J. D. A. Stainton 7677,
11 September 1975

The science of botany owes much to medicine and *vice versa*. From the beginning, the study of plants has been approached from these two standpoints – the purely philosophical on the one hand and the utilitarian on the other. In herbalism, these two branches join. From very early times (and even amongst some of the great apes) herbs were used as healing agents and careful study and examination has been necessary to distinguish one plant from another. It is really from this careful, but ultimately utilitarian, study that the science of systematics was born. Theophrastus, acknowledged as the father of botany, was one of several important Greek herbalists producing manuscripts about plants and their uses in the centuries before Christ. Dioscorides, living in Greece about the time of Christ, produced a work known as *De materia medica* – which was copied and re-copied by generations of doctors and botanists until into the sixteenth century. It was the standard of knowledge and was considered the foundation and groundwork of all study into plants and their properties. It is generally true that slavish adherence to authority, as was the case with Dioscorides, often hampers the progress of science, but in this case it led to preservation of the text and the knowledge contained therein through the Dark Ages – thus setting the stage of the great flowering of herbalism during the Renaissance. The advent of the printing press with moveable type in the middle of the fifteenth century allowed many copies of books to be produced and from that time onward herbals flourished in most parts of Europe. The herbalists recognised groups of plants often based upon their habitat 'Of trees which grow wild in the woods', by their medicinal or other chemical properties, 'Of poisonous plants', or very occasionally by the same characteristics we now use to recognise natural groups, 'Of umbelliferous plants'. The umbellifers were one of the first natural groups to be recognised by the herbalists. They did so using the form of the inflorescence – the shape of an umbrella. These sixteenth century botanists were certainly closely observing the structure of plants and using their observations to group plants together. Such groupings were not solely based on the plant's usefulness to man, but instead took into account intrinsic properties of the plants themselves. It is this observation of plant form and function and the translation of the information into systems of classification that let us truly call these Renaissance herbalists the fathers of modern scientific botany.

Algae, including both the seaweeds and many small unicellular forms, are traditionally considered to be plants. Students learn about them in botany classes, algal collections are housed in herbaria with plants, and phycologists – botanists who study algae – are usually found in botany departments. But many recent biology textbooks put the algae in the Kingdom Protista – a grab-bag of everything that is not plant, animal, bacteria or fungus. Some biologists however, align some of the traditional algae with plants, while other members of traditional algal groups are aligned with unicellular organisms like *Euglena*. Before the invention and widespread use of the electron microscope, which allows biologists to see ever more detail of cells and their structures, recognition of the major groups of unicellular organisms was relatively straightforward: algae were the 'mini-plants' and protozoa the 'mini-animals'. The incredible overlapping diversity found in those two apparently simple categories is astounding and has led to radical rethinking of the relationships and origins of these groups. Algae are traditionally divided into three basic types based on life cycle and pigment, the greens, the browns and the reds. Some of the algae, the greens, are in fact the closest relatives of the plants, while others, in particular the reds, are perhaps quite distantly related. The organisms we call the algae are a group of extremes, it contains both the longest and the smallest living organisms on Earth – some of the giant kelps of the northern seas are longer than the longest blue whale and some of the single-celled algae are the smallest nucleus-containing cells known. The red colour in the red algae comes from specialised photosynthetic pigments that absorb long wavelength blue and green light that penetrates deep into the ocean, thus allowing these organisms to live at depths of up to 250 metres below the surface. The algae, despite being perhaps a group of convenience rather than a natural evolutionary entity, continually amaze us with their diversity and serve as a reminder of how little we really know about the majority of organisms with whom we share planet Earth.

RHODOPHYTA:
Delesseria sanguinea
(Hudson) Lamouroux,
Great Britain, collected by J. H. Price,
25 May 1964

Acknowledgements

I owe an enormous debt of gratitude to my wife Charlotte. She has seen more pressed plant samples in the last three and a half years than a dedicated botanist would in a lifetime. Charlotte has searched high (the top cabinet only being accessible by ladder) and low (the bottom ones only accessible by kneeling) through millions of specimens, and has discovered some of the most beautiful plants either of us have ever seen. The selection of plants in this book reflects her innate sense of beauty, as I trust her judgement on such matters implicitly. No one else could have helped me distinguish between two equally beautiful but totally abstract forms.

Sandra Knapp who has been a veritable powerhouse of enthusiasm throughout this project and has provided us with such a brilliant and lighthearted text. Sandy introduced me to the unique and peculiar beauty of these specimens and has acted as a wonderful guide and teacher. Her obvious passion for her subject has made my own life much richer. Both Charlotte and I are privileged to have been her students.

I must also thank Brian Dowling, John Driscol, Howard Wakefield, Steve Seal, Emma Matheou, Guy Hearn, Sean Ellis, Claire Powell, Solve Sundsbo, Elaine Constantine, Kate Plumb and Emma Wheeler for their invaluable assistance whilst shooting and printing this project.

Both myself and Sandra Knapp would like to thank Professor Stephen Blackmore, Keeper of Botany at The Natural History Museum, for permission to use the collections in this way, and for his encouragement on this project. From the Botany Department at The Natural History Museum, our heartfelt thanks go to the following for their curation and help in finding specimens – Roy Vickery, Megan Lyall, Jenny Moore, Nick Turland, Caroline Whitefoord, Alison Paul, Len Ellis, Josephine Camus, Mary Chorley, Bob Press, Jodi Wheeler and Anne Hume.

N. K.

Schirmer/Mosel Verlag GmbH
Po box 40 17 23
8000 München 40, Germany
fax (0 89) 33 86 95

© images by Nick Knight, 1997
© text by The Natural History Museum, London, 1997
© this edition by Schirmer/Mosel, München, 1997/2000

A cip catalogue for this book is available from the British Library

No part of this publication may be reproduced in any form by any electronic or mechanical means (including photocopying, recording, or information storage and retrieval) without written permission from the publisher.

Separations: Nova Concept, Berlin
Typesetting: Typograph, Munich
Printing and binding: EBS, Verona

isbn 3-88814-910-x
A Schirmer/Mosel production